www.EffortlessMath.com

... So Much More Online!

✓ FREE Math lessons

✓ More Math learning books!

✓ Mathematics Worksheets

✓ Online Math Tutors

Need a PDF version of this book?

Send email to: Info@EffortlessMath.com

Ace the CHSPE Math in 30 Days

The Ultimate Crash Course to Beat the CHSPE Math Test

By

Reza Nazari

& Ava Ross

Welcome to
CHSPE Math Prep
2021

Thank you for choosing Effortless Math for your CHSPE Math test preparation and congratulations on making the decision to take the CHSPE test! It's a remarkable move you are taking, one that shouldn't be diminished in any capacity. That's why you need to use every tool possible to ensure you succeed on the test with the highest possible score, and this extensive study guide is one such tool.

If math has never been a strong subject for you, don't worry! This book will help you prepare for (and even ACE) the CHSPE test's math section. As test day draws nearer, effective preparation becomes increasingly more important. Thankfully, you have this comprehensive study guide to help you get ready for the test. With this guide, you can feel confident that you will be more than ready for the CHSPE Math test when the time comes.

First and foremost, it is important to note that this book is a study guide and not a textbook. It is best read from cover to cover. Every lesson of this "self-guided math book" was carefully developed to ensure that you are making the most effective use of your time while preparing for the test. This up-to-date guide reflects the 2021 test guidelines and will put you on the right track to hone your math skills, overcome exam anxiety, and boost your confidence, so that you can have your best to succeed on the CHSPE Math test.

This study guide will:

☑ Explain the format of the CHSPE Math test.

☑ Describe specific test-taking strategies that you can use on the test.

☑ Provide CHSPE Math test-taking tips.

☑ Review all CHSPE Math concepts and topics you will be tested on.

☑ Help you identify the areas in which you need to concentrate your study time.

☑ Offer exercises that help you develop the basic math skills you will learn in each section.

☑ Give **2 realistic and full-length practice tests** (featuring new question types) with detailed answers to help you measure your exam readiness and build confidence.

This resource contains everything you will ever need to succeed on the CHSPE Math test. You'll get in-depth instructions on every math topic as well as tips and techniques on how to answer each question type. You'll also get plenty of practice questions to boost your test-taking confidence.

In addition, in the following pages you'll find:

➢ **How to Use This Book Effectively** – This section provides you with step-by-step instructions on how to get the most out of this comprehensive study guide.

➢ **How to study for the CHSPE Math Test** – A six-step study program has been developed to help you make the best use of this book and prepare for your CHSPE Math test. Here you'll find tips and strategies to guide your study program and help you understand CHSPE Math and how to ace the test.

➢ **CHSPE Math Review** – Learn everything you need to know about the CHSPE Math test.

➢ **CHSPE Math Test-Taking Strategies** – Learn how to effectively put these recommended test-taking techniques into use for improving your CHSPE Math score.

➢ **Test Day Tips** – Review these tips to make sure you will do your best when the big day comes.

Effortless Math's CHSPE Online Center

Effortless Math Online CHSPE Center offers a complete study program, including the following:

✓ Step-by-step instructions on how to prepare for the CHSPE Math test

✓ Numerous CHSPE Math worksheets to help you measure your math skills

✓ Complete list of CHSPE Math formulas

✓ Video lessons for all CHSPE Math topics

✓ Full-length CHSPE Math practice tests

✓ And much more…

No Registration Required.

Visit **EffortlessMath.com/CHSPE** to find your online CHSPE Math resources.

How to Use This Book Effectively

Look no further when you need a study guide to improve your math skills to succeed on the math portion of the CHSPE test. Each chapter of this comprehensive guide to the CHSPE Math will provide you with the knowledge, tools, and understanding needed for every topic covered on the test.

It's imperative that you understand each topic before moving onto another one, as that's the way to guarantee your success. Each chapter provides you with examples and a step-by-step guide of every concept to better understand the content that will be on the test. To get the best possible results from this book:

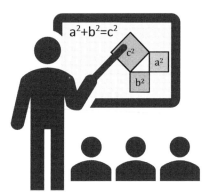

➢ **Begin studying long before your test date**. This provides you ample time to learn the different math concepts. The earlier you begin studying for the test, the sharper your skills will be. Do not procrastinate! Provide yourself with plenty of time (at least 30 days) to learn the concepts and feel comfortable that you understand them when your test date arrives.

➢ **Practice consistently**. Study CHSPE Math concepts at least 20 to 30 minutes a day. Remember, slow and steady wins the race, which can be applied to preparing for the CHSPE Math test. Instead of cramming to tackle everything at once, be patient and learn the math topics in short bursts.

➢ Whenever you get a math problem wrong, **mark it off, and review it later** to make sure you understand the concept.

➢ Start each session by **looking over the previous material.**

➢ Once you've reviewed the book's lessons, **take a practice test** on Day 29 to gauge your level of readiness. Then, review your results. Read detailed answers and solutions for each question you missed.

➢ **Take another practice test** (on Day 30) to get an idea of how ready you are to take the actual exam. Taking the practice tests will give you the confidence you need on test day. Simulate the CHSPE testing environment by sitting in a quiet room free from distraction. Make sure to clock yourself with a timer.

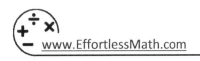

How to Study for the CHSPE Math Test

Studying for the CHSPE Math test can be a really daunting and boring task. What's the best way to go about it? Is there a certain study method that works better than others? Well, studying for the CHSPE Math can be done effectively. The following six-step program has been designed to make preparing for the CHSPE Math test more efficient and less overwhelming.

Step **1** - Create a study plan
Step **2** - Choose your study resources
Step **3** - Review, Learn, Practice
Step **4** - Learn and practice test-taking strategies
Step **5** - Learn the CHSPE Test format and take practice tests
Step **6** - Analyze your performance

STEP 1: Create a Study Plan

It's always easier to get things done when you have a plan. Creating a study plan for the CHSPE Math test can help you to stay on track with your studies. It's important to sit down and prepare a study plan with what works with your life, work, and any other obligations you may have. Devote enough time each day to studying. It's also a great idea to break down each section of the exam into blocks and study one concept at a time.

It's important to understand that there is no "right" way to create a study plan. Your study plan will be personalized based on your specific needs and learning style.

Follow these guidelines to create an effective study plan for your CHSPE Math test:

★ **Analyze your learning style and study habits** – Everyone has a different learning style. It is essential to embrace your individuality and the unique way you learn. Think about what works and what doesn't work for you. Do you prefer CHSPE Math prep books or a combination of textbooks and video lessons? Does it work better for you if you study every night for thirty minutes or is it more effective to study in the morning before going to work?

★ **Evaluate your schedule** – Review your current schedule and find out how much time you can consistently devote to CHSPE Math study.

★ **Develop a schedule** – Now it's time to add your study schedule to your calendar like any other obligation. Schedule time for study, practice, and review. Plan out which topic you will study on which day to ensure that you're devoting enough time to each concept. Develop a study plan that is mindful, realistic, and flexible.

★ **Stick to your schedule** – A study plan is only effective when it is followed consistently. You should try to develop a study plan that you can follow for the length of your study program.

★ **Evaluate your study plan and adjust as needed** – Sometimes you need to adjust your plan when you have new commitments. Check in with yourself regularly to make sure that you're not falling behind in your study plan. Remember, the most important thing is sticking to your plan. Your study plan is all about helping you be more productive. If you find that your study plan is not as effective as you want, don't get discouraged. It's okay to make changes as you figure out what works best for you.

STEP 2: Choose Your Study Resources

There are numerous textbooks and online resources available for the CHSPE Math test, and it may not be clear where to begin. Don't worry! This study guide provides everything you need to fully prepare for your CHSPE Math test. In addition to the book content, you can also use Effortless Math's online resources. (video lessons, worksheets, formulas, etc.)

Simply visit <u>EffortlessMath.com/CHSPE</u> to find your online CHSPE Math resources.

STEP 3: Review, Learn, Practice

This CHSPE Math study guide breaks down each subject into specific skills or content areas. For instance, the percent concept is separated into different topics—percent calculation, percent increase and decrease, percent problems, etc. Use this book to help you go over all key math concepts and topics on the CHSPE Math test.

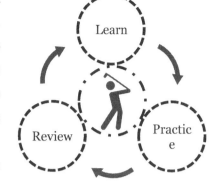

As you read each chapter, take notes or highlight the concepts you would like to go over again in the future. If you're unfamiliar with a topic or something is difficult for you, do additional research on it. For each math topic, plenty of instructions, step-by-step guides, and examples are provided to ensure you get a good grasp of the material. You can also find video lessons on the Effortless Math website for each CHSPE Math concept. Quickly review the topics you do understand to get a brush-up of the material. Be sure to do the practice questions provided at the end of every chapter to measure your understanding of the concepts.

STEP 4: Learn and Practice Test-taking Strategies

In the following sections, you will find important test-taking strategies and tips that can help you earn extra points. You'll learn how to think strategically and when to guess if you don't know the answer to a question. Using CHSPE Math test-taking strategies and tips can help you raise your score and do well on the test. Apply test taking strategies on the practice tests to help you boost your confidence.

STEP 5: Learn the CHSPE Test Format and Take Practice Tests

The CHSPE *Test Review* section provides information about the structure of the CHSPE test. Read this section to learn more about the CHSPE test structure, different test sections, the number of questions in each section, and the section time limits. When you have a prior understanding of the test format and different types of CHSPE Math questions, you'll feel more confident when you take the actual exam.

Once you have read through the instructions and lessons and feel like you are ready to go – take advantage of both of the full-length CHSPE Math practice tests available in this study guide on Days 29 and 30. Use the practice tests to sharpen your skills and build confidence.

The CHSPE Math practice tests offered at the end of the book are formatted similarly to the actual CHSPE Math test. When you take each practice test, try to simulate actual testing conditions. To take the practice tests, sit in a quiet space, time yourself, and work through as many of the questions as time allows. The practice tests are followed by detailed answer explanations to help you find your weak areas, learn from your mistakes, and raise your CHSPE Math score.

STEP 6: Analyze Your Performance

After taking the practice tests, look over the answer keys and explanations to learn which questions you answered correctly and which you did not. Never be discouraged if you make a few mistakes. See them as a learning opportunity. This will highlight your strengths and weaknesses.

You can use the results to determine if you need additional practice or if you are ready to take the actual CHSPE Math test.

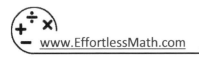

Looking for more?

Visit <u>EffortlessMath.com/ CHSPE</u> to find hundreds of CHSPE Math worksheets, video tutorials, practice tests, CHSPE Math formulas, and much more.

Or scan this QR code.

No Registration Required.

CHSPE Test Review

The California High School Proficiency Examination (knows as CHSPE) is a test for students in California to verify their high school level skills. Students take the CHSPE to leave high school early or to attend college. Test takers who pass the CHSPE receive a diploma equivalent entitled Certificate of Proficiency, from the California State Board of Education.

There are two sections on CHSPE:

o English Language Arts
o Mathematics

The Mathematics section of CHSPE contains 50 multiple-choice questions assess content in the following areas:

• Number Sense and Operations
• Patterns, Relationships, And Algebra
• Data, Statistics, And Probability
• Geometry and Measurement

A basic calculator is allowed in the mathematics section of CHSPE. Test takers have a total of 3.5 hours to take the CHSPE. No part of the exam is timed, and you may spend as much time as you like on any portion until the testing session ends.

CHSPE Math Test-Taking Strategies

Here are some test-taking strategies that you can use to maximize your performance and results on the CHSPE Math test.

#1: USE THIS APPROACH TO ANSWER EVERY CHSPE MATH QUESTION

- Review the question to identify keywords and important information.

- Translate the keywords into math operations so you can solve the problem.

- Review the answer choices. What are the differences between answer choices?

- Draw or label a diagram if needed.

- Try to find patterns.

- Find the right method to answer the question. Use straightforward math, plug in numbers, or test the answer choices (backsolving).

- Double-check your work.

#2: USE EDUCATED GUESSING

This approach is applicable to the problems you understand to some degree but cannot solve using straightforward math. In such cases, try to filter out as many answer choices as possible before picking an answer. In cases where you don't have a clue about what a certain problem entails, don't waste any time trying to eliminate answer choices. Just choose one randomly before moving onto the next question.

As you can ascertain, direct solutions are the most optimal approach. Carefully read through the question, determine what the solution is using the math you have learned before, then coordinate the answer with one of the choices available to you. Are you stumped? Make your best guess, then move on.

Don't leave any fields empty! Even if you're unable to work out a problem, strive to answer it. Take a guess if you have to. You will not lose points by getting an answer wrong, though you may gain a point by getting it correct!

#3 : BALLPARK

A ballpark answer is a rough approximation. When we become overwhelmed by calculations and figures, we end up making silly mistakes. A decimal that is moved by one unit can change an answer from right to wrong, regardless of the number of steps that you went through to get it. That's where ballparking can play a big part.

If you think you know what the correct answer may be (even if it's just a ballpark answer), you'll usually have the ability to eliminate a couple of choices. While answer choices are usually based on the average student error and/or values that are closely tied, you will still be able to weed out choices that are way far afield. Try to find answers that aren't in the proverbial ballpark when you're looking for a wrong answer on a multiple-choice question. This is an optimal approach to eliminating answers to a problem.

#4 : BACKSOLVING

All questions on the CHSPE Math test will be in multiple-choice format. Many test-takers prefer multiple-choice questions, as at least the answer is right there. You'll typically have four answers to pick from. You simply need to figure out which one is correct. Usually, the best way to go about doing so is "backsolving."

As mentioned earlier, direct solutions are the most optimal approach to answering a question. Carefully read through a problem, calculate a solution, then correspond the answer with one of the choices displayed in front of you. If you can't calculate a solution, your next best approach involves "backsolving."

When backsolving a problem, contrast one of your answer options against the problem you are asked, then see which of them is most relevant. More often than not, answer choices are listed in ascending or descending order. In such cases, try out the choices B or C. If it's not correct, you can go either down or up from there.

#5 : PLUGGING IN NUMBERS

"Plugging in numbers" is a strategy that can be applied to a wide range of different math problems on the CHSPE Math test. This approach is typically used to simplify a challenging question so that it is more understandable. By using the strategy carefully, you can find the answer without too much trouble.

The concept is fairly straightforward—replace unknown variables in a problem with certain values. When selecting a number, consider the following:

- Choose a number that's basic (just not too basic). Generally, you should avoid choosing 1 (or even 0). A decent choice is 2.

- Try not to choose a number that is displayed in the problem.

- Make sure you keep your numbers different if you need to choose at least two of them.

- More often than not, choosing numbers merely lets you filter out some of your answer choices. As such, don't just go with the first choice that gives you the right answer.

- If several answers seem correct, then you'll need to choose another value and try again. This time, though, you'll just need to check choices that haven't been eliminated yet.

- If your question contains fractions, then a potential right answer may involve either an LCD (least common denominator) or an LCD multiple.

- 100 is the number you should choose when you are dealing with problems involving percentages.

CHSPE Mathematics Test – Daytime Tips

After practicing and reviewing all the math concepts you've been taught, and taking some CHSPE mathematics practice tests, you'll be prepared for test day. Consider the following tips to be extra-ready come test time.

Before Your Test

What to do the night before:

- **Relax!** One day before your test, study lightly or skip studying altogether. You shouldn't attempt to learn something new, either. There are plenty of reasons why studying the evening before a big test can work against you. Put it this way–a marathoner wouldn't go out for a sprint before the day of a big race. Mental marathoners–such as yourself–should not study for any more than one hour 24 hours before a CHSPE test. That's because your brain requires some rest to be at its best. The night before your exam, spend some time with family or friends, or read a book.

- **Avoid bright screens** - You'll have to get some good shuteye the night before your test. Bright screens (such as the ones coming from your laptop, TV, or mobile device) should be avoided altogether. Staring at such a screen will keep your brain up, making it hard to drift asleep at a reasonable hour.

- **Make sure your dinner is healthy** - The meal that you have for dinner should be nutritious. Be sure to drink plenty of water as well. Load up on your complex carbohydrates, much like a marathon runner would do. Pasta, rice, and potatoes are ideal options here, as are vegetables and protein sources.

- **Get your bag ready for test day** - The night prior to your test, pack your bag with your stationery, admissions pass, ID, and any other gear that you need. Keep the bag right by your front door.

- **Make plans to reach the testing site** - Before going to sleep, ensure that you understand precisely how you will arrive at the site of the test. If parking is something you'll have to find first, plan for it. If you're dependent on public transit, then review the schedule. You should also make sure that the train/bus/subway/streetcar you use will be running. Find out about road closures as well. If a parent or friend is accompanying you, ensure that they understand what steps they have to take as well.

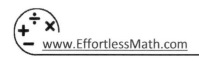

The Day of the Test

■ **Get up reasonably early, but not too early.**

■ **Have breakfast** - Breakfast improves your concentration, memory, and mood. As such, make sure the breakfast that you eat in the morning is healthy. The last thing you want to be is distracted by a grumbling tummy. If it's not your own stomach making those noises, another test taker close to you might be instead. Prevent discomfort or embarrassment by consuming a healthy breakfast. Bring a snack with you if you think you'll need it.

■ **Follow your daily routine** - Do you watch Good Morning America each morning while getting ready for the day? Don't break your usual habits on the day of the test. Likewise, if coffee isn't something you drink in the morning, then don't take up the habit hours before your test. Routine consistency lets you concentrate on the main objective–doing the best you can on your test.

■ **Wear layers** - Dress yourself up in comfortable layers. You should be ready for any kind of internal temperature. If it gets too warm during the test, take a layer off.

■ **Get there on time** - The last thing you want to do is get to the test site late. Rather, you should be there 45 minutes prior to the start of the test. Upon your arrival, try not to hang out with anybody who is nervous. Any anxious energy they exhibit shouldn't influence you.

■ **Leave the books at home** - No books should be brought to the test site. If you start developing anxiety before the test, books could encourage you to do some last-minute studying, which will only hinder you. Keep the books far away–better yet, leave them at home.

■ **Make your voice heard** - If something is off, speak to a proctor. If medical attention is needed or if you'll require anything, consult the proctor prior to the start of the test. Any doubts you have should be clarified. You should be entering the test site with a state of mind that is completely clear.

■ **Have faith in yourself** - When you feel confident, you will be able to perform at your best. When you are waiting for the test to begin, envision yourself receiving an outstanding result. Try to see yourself as someone who knows all the answers, no matter what the questions are. A lot of athletes tend to use this technique–particularly before a big competition. Your expectations will be reflected by your performance.

During your test

■ **Be calm and breathe deeply** - You need to relax before the test, and some deep breathing will go a long way to help you do that. Be confident and calm. You got this. Everybody feels a little stressed out just before an evaluation of any kind is set to begin. Learn some effective breathing exercises. Spend a minute meditating before the test starts. Filter out any negative thoughts you have. Exhibit confidence when having such thoughts.

■ **Concentrate on the test** - Refrain from comparing yourself to anyone else. You shouldn't be distracted by the people near you or random noise. Concentrate exclusively on the test. If you find yourself irritated by surrounding noises, earplugs can be used to block sounds off close to you. Don't forget–the test is going to last several hours if you're taking more than one subject of the test. Some of that time will be dedicated to brief sections. Concentrate on the specific section you are working on during a particular moment. Do not let your mind wander off to upcoming or previous sections.

■ **Try to answer each question individually** - Focus only on the question you are working on. Use one of the test-taking strategies to solve the problem. If you aren't able to come up with an answer, don't get frustrated. Simply skip that question, then move onto the next one.

■ **Don't forget to breathe!** Whenever you notice your mind wandering, your stress levels boosting, or frustration brewing, take a thirty-second break. Shut your eyes, drop your pencil, breathe deeply, and let your shoulders relax. You will end up being more productive when you allow yourself to relax for a moment.

■ **Review your answer.** If you still have time at the end of the test, don't waste it. Go back and check over your answers. It is worth going through the test from start to finish to ensure that you didn't make a sloppy mistake somewhere.

- **Optimize your breaks** - When break time comes, use the restroom, have a snack, and reactivate your energy for the subsequent section. Doing some stretches can help stimulate your blood flow.

After your test

- **Take it easy** - You will need to set some time aside to relax and decompress once the test has concluded. There is no need to stress yourself out about what you could've said, or what you may have done wrong. At this point, there's nothing you can do about it. Your energy and time would be better spent on something that will bring you happiness for the remainder of your day.

- **Redoing the test** - Did you pass the test? Congratulations! Your hard work paid off!

  If you have failed your test, though, don't worry! The test can be retaken. In such cases, you will need to follow the retake policy. You also need to re-register to take the exam again.

contents

Day 1: Whole Numbers

Math Topics that you'll learn today:

- ✓ Rounding
- ✓ Whole Number Addition and Subtraction
- ✓ Whole Number Multiplication and Division
- ✓ Rounding and Estimates

Rounding

Step-by-step guide:

Rounding is putting a number up or down to the nearest whole number or the nearest hundred, etc.

- ✓ First, find the place value you'll round to.
- ✓ Find the digit to the right of the place value you're rounding to. If it is 5 or bigger, add 1 to the place value you're rounding to and put zero for all digits on its right side. If the digit to the right of the place value is less than 5, keep the place value and put zero for all digits to the right.

Examples:

1) Round 64 to the nearest ten.

The place value of ten is 6. The digit on the right side is 4 (which is less than 5). Keep 6 and put zero for the digit on the right side. The answer is 60. 64 rounded to the nearest ten is 60, because 64 is closer to 60 than to 70.

2) Round 694 to the nearest hundred.

694 rounded to the nearest hundred is 700, because the digit on the right side of hundred place is 9. Add 1 to 6 and put zeros for other digits. The answer is 700.

✍ Round each number to the nearest ten.

1) 84 = ____   4) 63 = ____
2) 70 = ____   5) 79 = ____
3) 47 = ____   6) 55 = ____

✍ Round each number to the nearest hundred.

7) 185 = ____   10) 109 = ____
8) 254 = ____   11) 222 = ____
9) 729 = ____   12) 311 = ____

Whole Number Addition and Subtraction

Step-by-step guide:

- ✓ Line up the numbers.
- ✓ Start with the unit place. (ones place)
- ✓ Regroup if necessary.
- ✓ Add or subtract the tens place.
- ✓ Continue with other digits.

Examples:

1) Find the sum. $285 + 145 = ?$

First line up the numbers: $\begin{array}{r} 285 \\ + 145 \\ \hline \end{array}$ → Start with the unit place. (ones place) $5 + 5 = 10$,

Write 0 for ones place and keep 1, $\begin{array}{r} 1 \\ 285 \\ + 145 \\ \hline 0 \end{array}$, Add the tens place and the digit 1 we kept:

$1 + 8 + 4 = 13$, Write 3 and keep 1, $\begin{array}{r} 1\,1 \\ 285 \\ + 145 \\ \hline 30 \end{array}$

Continue with other digits → $1 + 2 + 1 = 4$ → $\begin{array}{r} 1\,1 \\ 285 \\ + 145 \\ \hline 430 \end{array}$

2) Find the difference. $976 - 453 = ?$

First line up the numbers: $\begin{array}{r} 976 \\ - 453 \\ \hline \end{array}$, → Start with the unit place. $6 - 3 = 3$, $\begin{array}{r} 976 \\ - 453 \\ \hline 3 \end{array}$,

Subtract the tens place. $7 - 5 = 2$, $\begin{array}{r} 976 \\ - 453 \\ \hline 23 \end{array}$, Continue with other digits → $9 - 4 = 5$, $\begin{array}{r} 976 \\ - 453 \\ \hline 523 \end{array}$

✍ Find the sum or difference.

1) $1,264 + 856 =$ 5) $2,170 + 245 =$

2) $2,689 - 456 =$ 6) $3,221 + 2,560 =$

3) $1,432 - 556 =$ 7) $3,788 + 1,892 =$

4) $2,820 + 464 =$ 8) $4,238 + 2,576 =$

Whole Number Multiplication

Step-by-step guide:

- ✓ Learn the times tables first! To solve multiplication problems fast, you need to memorize the times table. For example, 3 times 8 is 24 or 8 times 7 is 56.
- ✓ For multiplication, line up the numbers you are multiplying.
- ✓ Start with the ones place and regroup if necessary.
- ✓ Continue with other digits.

Examples:

1) Solve. $500 \times 30 = ?$

Line up the numbers: $\begin{array}{r} 500 \\ \times\, 30 \\ \hline \end{array}$, start with the ones place $\rightarrow 0 \times 500 = 0$, $\begin{array}{r} 500 \\ \times\, 30 \\ \hline 0 \end{array}$, Continue

with other digit which is 3. $\rightarrow 500 \times 3 = 1,500$, $\begin{array}{r} 500 \\ \times\, 30 \\ \hline 1,5000 \end{array}$

2) Solve. $820 \times 25 = ?$

Line up the numbers: $\begin{array}{r} 820 \\ \times\, 25 \\ \hline \end{array}$, start with the ones place $\rightarrow 5 \times 0 = 0$, $\begin{array}{r} 820 \\ \times\, 25 \\ \hline 0 \end{array}$, $5 \times 2 = 10$,

write 0 and keep 1. $\begin{array}{r} 820 \\ \times\, 25 \\ \hline 00 \end{array}$, $\rightarrow 5 \times 8 = 40$, add 1 to 40, the answer is 41. $\begin{array}{r} 820 \\ \times\, 25 \\ \hline 4,100 \end{array}$

Now, write 0 in the next line and multiply 820 by 2, using the same process. (Since 2 is in the tens place, we need to write 0 before doing the operation). The answer is 16,400. Add 4,100 and 16,400. The answer is: $4,100 + 16,400 = 20,500$

✎ *Find the missing number.*

1) $24 \times 5 = $ _____
2) $28 \times 8 = $ _____
3) $360 \times 6 = $ _____
4) $500 \times 12 = $ _____

5) $144 \times 51 = $ _____
6) $238 \times 18 = $ _____
7) $362 \times 14 = $ _____
8) $238 \times 28 = $ _____

Whole Number Division

Step-by-step guide:

Division: A typical division problem: Dividend ÷ Divisor = Quotient

- In division, we want to find how many times a number (divisor) is contained in another number (dividend). The result in a division problem is the quotient.
- ✓ First, write the problem in division format. (dividend is inside; divisor is outside)

$$\text{Divisor} \overline{\big)\text{Dividend}}^{\text{Quotient}}$$

- ✓ Now, find how many times divisor goes into dividend. (if it is a big number, break the dividend into smaller numbers by choosing the appropriate number of digits from left. Start from the first digit on the left side of the divided and see if the divisor will go into it. If not, keep moving over one digit to the right in the dividend until you have a number the divisor will go into.
- ✓ Find number of times the divisor goes into the part of the dividend you chose.
- ✓ Write the answer above the digit in the dividend you are using and multiply it by the divisor and Write the product under the part of the dividend you are using, then subtract.
- ✓ Bring down the next digit in the dividend and repeat this process until you have nothing left to bring down.

Example: Solve. $234 \div 4 = ?$

$$4 \overline{\big)\,234}$$

- ✓ First, write the problem in division format.
- ✓ Start from left digit of the dividend. 4 doesn't go into 2. So, choose another digit of the dividend. It is 3.
- ✓ Now, find how many times 4 goes into 23. The answer is 5.
- ✓ Write 5 above the dividend part. 4 times 5 is 20. Write 20 below 23 and subtract. The answer is 3.

$$4 \overline{\big)\,234}^{\,5}$$

- ✓ Now bring down the next digit which is 4. How many times 4 goes into 34? The answer is 8. Write 8 above dividend. This is the final step since there is no other digit of the dividend to bring down. The final answer is 58 and the remainder is 2.

$$
\begin{array}{r}
58 \\
4 \overline{\big)\,234} \\
-20 \\
\hline
34 \\
-32 \\
\hline
2
\end{array}
$$

✍ Solve.

1) $240 \div 5 = $ _____
2) $280 \div 4 = $ _____
3) $562 \div 8 = $ _____
4) $522 \div 9 = $ _____
5) $834 \div 8 = $ _____
6) $922 \div 12 = $ _____
7) $880 \div 15 = $ _____
8) $721 \div 22 = $ _____

Rounding and Estimates

Step-by-step guide:

Rounding and estimating are math strategies used for approximating a number. To estimate means to make a rough guess or calculation. To round means to simplify a known number by scaling it slightly up or down.

✓ To estimate a math operation, round the numbers.
✓ For 2-digit numbers, your usually can round to the nearest tens, for 3-digit numbers, round to nearest hundreds, etc.
✓ Find the answer.

Examples:

1) Estimate the sum by rounding each number to the nearest hundred. $153 + 426 =?$
153 rounded to the nearest hundred is 200. 426 rounded to the nearest hundred is 400. Then: $200 + 400 = 600$

2) Estimate the result by rounding each number to the nearest ten. $38 - 26 = ?$
38 rounded to the nearest ten is 40. 25 rounded to the nearest ten is 30. Then: $40 - 30 = 10$

Estimate the sum by rounding each number to the nearest ten.

1) $14 + 68 =$ _____

2) $82 + 12 =$ _____

3) $43 + 66 =$ _____

4) $47 + 69 =$ _____

5) $553 + 231 =$ _____

6) $418 + 849 =$ _____

Estimate the product by rounding each number to the nearest ten.

7) $55 \times 62 =$ _____

8) $14 \times 27 =$ _____

9) $34 \times 66 =$ _____

10) $18 \times 12 =$ _____

11) $62 \times 53 =$ _____

12) $41 \times 26 =$ _____

Answers – Day 1

Rounding

1) 80
2) 70
3) 50
4) 60

5) 80
6) 60
7) 200
8) 300

9) 700
10) 100
11) 200
12) 300

Whole Number Addition and Subtraction

1) 2,120
2) 2,233
3) 876

4) 3,284
5) 2,415
6) 5,781

7) 5,680
8) 6,814

Whole Number Multiplication

1) 120
2) 224
3) 2,160

4) 6,000
5) 7,344
6) 4,284

7) 5,068
8) 6,664

Whole Number Division

1) 48
2) 70
3) 70, r2

4) 58
5) 104, 2
6) 76, r10

7) 58, r10
8) 32, r17

Rounding and Estimates

1) 80
2) 90
3) 110
4) 120

5) 780
6) 1,270
7) 3,600
8) 300

9) 2,100
10) 200
11) 3,000
12) 1,200

Day 2: Fractions

Math Topics that you'll learn today:

- ✓ Simplifying Fractions

- ✓ Adding and Subtracting Fractions

- ✓ Multiplying and Dividing Fractions

"A Man is like a fraction whose numerator is what he is and whose denominator is what he thinks of himself. The larger the denominator, the smaller the fraction." -Tolstoy

Simplifying Fractions

Step-by-step guide:

✓ Evenly divide both the top and bottom of the fraction by $2, 3, 5, 7, \ldots$ etc.

✓ Continue until you can't go any further.

Examples:

1) Simplify $\frac{12}{20}$.

To simplify $\frac{12}{20}$, find a number that both 12 and 20 are divisible by. Both are divisible by 4.

Then: $\frac{12}{20} = \frac{12 \div 4}{20 \div 4} = \frac{3}{5}$

2) Simplify $\frac{64}{80}$.

To simplify $\frac{64}{80}$, find a number that both 64 and 80 are divisible by. Both are divisible by 8 and

16. Then: $\frac{64}{80} = \frac{64 \div 8}{80 \div 8} = \frac{8}{10}$, 8 and 10 are divisible by 2, then: $\frac{8}{10} = \frac{4}{5}$

or $\frac{64}{80} = \frac{64 \div 16}{80 \div 16} = \frac{4}{5}$

✎ *Simplify each fraction.*

1) $\frac{9}{18} =$

2) $\frac{8}{10} =$

3) $\frac{6}{8} =$

4) $\frac{5}{20} =$

5) $\frac{18}{24} =$

6) $\frac{6}{9} =$

7) $\frac{12}{15} =$

8) $\frac{4}{16} =$

9) $\frac{18}{36} =$

10) $\frac{6}{42} =$

11) $\frac{13}{39} =$

12) $\frac{21}{28} =$

Adding and Subtracting Fractions

Step-by-step guide:

- ✓ For "like" fractions (fractions with the same denominator), add or subtract the numerators and write the answer over the common denominator.
- ✓ Find equivalent fractions with the same denominator before you can add or subtract fractions with different denominators.
- ✓ Adding and Subtracting with the same denominator:

$$\frac{a}{b} + \frac{c}{b} = \frac{a+c}{b} , \frac{a}{b} - \frac{c}{b} = \frac{a-c}{b}$$

- ✓ Adding and Subtracting fractions with different denominators:

$$\frac{a}{b} + \frac{c}{d} = \frac{ad+c}{bd} , \frac{a}{b} - \frac{c}{d} = \frac{ad-cb}{bd}$$

Examples:

1) Subtract fractions. $\frac{4}{5} - \frac{3}{5} =$

For "like" fractions, subtract the numerators and write the answer over the common denominator. then: $\frac{4}{5} - \frac{3}{5} = \frac{1}{5}$

2) Subtract fractions. $\frac{2}{3} - \frac{1}{2} =$

For "unlike" fractions, find equivalent fractions with the same denominator before you can add or subtract fractions with different denominators. Use this formula: $\frac{a}{b} - \frac{c}{d} = \frac{ad-cb}{bd}$

$\frac{2}{3} - \frac{1}{2} = \frac{(2)(2)-(1)(3)}{3 \times 2} = \frac{4-3}{6} = \frac{1}{6}$

✎ *Find the sum or difference.*

1) $\frac{1}{3} + \frac{2}{3} =$ 4) $\frac{3}{7} + \frac{2}{3} =$ 7) $\frac{2}{3} - \frac{1}{6} =$

2) $\frac{1}{2} + \frac{1}{3} =$ 5) $\frac{1}{2} - \frac{1}{3} =$ 8) $\frac{3}{5} - \frac{1}{2} =$

3) $\frac{2}{5} + \frac{1}{2} =$ 6) $\frac{4}{5} - \frac{2}{3} =$ 9) $\frac{8}{9} - \frac{2}{5} =$

Multiplying and Dividing Fractions

Step-by-step guide:

- ✓ Multiplying fractions: multiply the top numbers and multiply the bottom numbers.
- ✓ Dividing fractions: Keep, Change, Flip
- ✓ Keep first fraction, change division sign to multiplication, and flip the numerator and denominator of the second fraction. Then, solve!

Examples:

1) Multiplying fractions. $\frac{5}{6} \times \frac{3}{4} =$

Multiply the top numbers and multiply the bottom numbers.

$\frac{5}{6} \times \frac{3}{4} = \frac{5 \times 3}{6 \times 4} = \frac{15}{24}$, simplify: $\frac{15}{24} = \frac{15 \div 3}{24 \div 3} = \frac{5}{8}$

2) Dividing fractions. $\frac{1}{4} \div \frac{2}{3} =$

Keep first fraction, change division sign to multiplication, and flip the numerator and denominator of the second fraction. Then: $\frac{1}{4} \times \frac{3}{2} = \frac{1 \times 3}{4 \times 2} = \frac{3}{8}$

✎ Find the answers.

1) $\frac{1}{2} \times \frac{3}{4} =$

2) $\frac{3}{5} \times \frac{2}{3} =$

3) $\frac{1}{4} \times \frac{2}{5} =$

4) $\frac{1}{6} \times \frac{4}{5} =$

5) $\frac{1}{5} \times \frac{1}{4} =$

6) $\frac{2}{5} \times \frac{1}{2} =$

7) $\frac{1}{2} \div \frac{1}{4} =$

8) $\frac{1}{3} \div \frac{1}{2} =$

9) $\frac{2}{5} \div \frac{1}{3} =$

10) $\frac{1}{4} \div \frac{2}{3} =$

11) $\frac{1}{5} \div \frac{3}{10} =$

12) $\frac{2}{7} \div \frac{1}{3} =$

Answers – Day 2

Simplifying Fractions

1) $\frac{1}{2}$

2) $\frac{4}{5}$

3) $\frac{3}{4}$

4) $\frac{1}{4}$

5) $\frac{3}{4}$

6) $\frac{2}{3}$

7) $\frac{4}{5}$

8) $\frac{1}{4}$

9) $\frac{1}{2}$

10) $\frac{1}{7}$

11) $\frac{1}{3}$

12) $\frac{3}{4}$

Adding and Subtracting Fractions

1) $\frac{3}{3} = 1$

2) $\frac{5}{6}$

3) $\frac{9}{10}$

4) $\frac{23}{21}$

5) $\frac{1}{6}$

6) $\frac{2}{15}$

7) $\frac{1}{2}$

8) $\frac{1}{10}$

9) $\frac{22}{45}$

Multiplying and Dividing Fractions

1) $\frac{3}{8}$

2) $\frac{2}{5}$

3) $\frac{1}{10}$

4) $\frac{2}{15}$

5) $\frac{1}{20}$

6) $\frac{1}{5}$

7) 2

8) $\frac{2}{3}$

9) $\frac{6}{5}$

10) $\frac{3}{8}$

11) $\frac{2}{3}$

12) $\frac{6}{7}$

Day 3: Mixed Numbers

Math Topics that you'll learn today:

- ✓ Adding Mixed Numbers

- ✓ Subtracting Mixed Numbers

- ✓ Multiplying Mixed Numbers

- ✓ Dividing Mixed Numbers

"Wherever there is number, there is beauty." -Proclus

Adding Mixed Numbers

Step-by-step guide:

Use the following steps for both adding and subtracting mixed numbers.
- ✓ Add whole numbers of the mixed numbers.
- ✓ Add the fractions of each mixed number.
- ✓ Find the Least Common Denominator (LCD) if necessary.
- ✓ Add whole numbers and fractions.
- ✓ Write your answer in lowest terms.

Examples:

1) Add mixed numbers. $1\frac{3}{4} + 2\frac{3}{8} =$

Rewriting our equation with parts separated, $1 + \frac{3}{4} + 2 + \frac{3}{8}$, Solving the whole number parts $1 + 2 = 3$, Solving the fraction parts $\frac{3}{4} + \frac{3}{8}$, and rewrite to solve with the equivalent fractions.

$\frac{6}{8} + \frac{3}{8} = \frac{9}{8} = 1\frac{1}{8}$, then Combining the whole and fraction parts $3 + 1 + \frac{1}{8} = 4\frac{1}{8}$

2) Add mixed numbers. $1\frac{2}{3} + 4\frac{1}{6} =$

Rewriting our equation with parts separated, $1 + \frac{2}{3} + 4 + \frac{1}{6}$, Solving the whole number parts $1 + 4 = 5$, Solving the fraction parts $\frac{2}{3} + \frac{1}{6}$, and rewrite to solve with the equivalent fractions.

$\frac{4}{6} + \frac{1}{6} = \frac{5}{6}$, then Combining the whole and fraction parts $5 + \frac{5}{6} = 5\frac{5}{6}$

✍ Find the sum.

1) $2\frac{1}{2} + 1\frac{1}{3} =$

2) $6\frac{1}{2} + 3\frac{1}{2} =$

3) $2\frac{3}{8} + 3\frac{1}{8} =$

4) $4\frac{1}{2} + 1\frac{1}{4} =$

5) $1\frac{3}{7} + 1\frac{5}{14} =$

6) $6\frac{5}{12} + 3\frac{3}{4} =$

7) $5\frac{1}{2} + 8\frac{3}{4} =$

8) $3\frac{7}{8} + 3\frac{1}{3} =$

9) $3\frac{3}{9} + 7\frac{6}{11} =$

Subtract Mixed Numbers

Step-by-step guide:

Use the following steps for both adding and subtracting mixed numbers.

✓ Subtract the whole number of second mixed number from whole number of the first mixed number.
✓ Subtract the second fraction from the first one.
✓ Find the Least Common Denominator (LCD) if necessary.
✓ Add the result of whole numbers and fractions.
✓ Write your answer in lowest terms.

Examples:

1) Subtract. $5\frac{2}{3} - 2\frac{1}{4} =$

Rewriting our equation with parts separated, $5 + \frac{2}{3} - 2 - \frac{1}{4}$

Solving the whole number parts $5 - 2 = 3$, Solving the fraction parts, $\frac{2}{3} - \frac{1}{4} = \frac{8-3}{12} = \frac{5}{12}$

Combining the whole and fraction parts, $3 + \frac{5}{12} = 3\frac{5}{12}$

2) Subtract. $3\frac{4}{5} - 1\frac{1}{2} =$

Rewriting our equation with parts separated, $3 + \frac{4}{5} - 1 - \frac{1}{2}$

Solving the whole number parts $3 - 1 = 2$, Solving the fraction parts, $\frac{4}{5} - \frac{1}{2} = \frac{8-5}{10} = \frac{3}{10}$

Combining the whole and fraction parts, $2 + \frac{3}{10} = 2\frac{3}{10}$

✏ *Find the difference.*

1) $3\frac{1}{3} - 1\frac{1}{3} =$

2) $4\frac{1}{2} - 3\frac{1}{2} =$

3) $5\frac{1}{2} - 2\frac{1}{4} =$

4) $6\frac{1}{6} - 5\frac{1}{3} =$

5) $8\frac{1}{2} - 1\frac{1}{10} =$

6) $9\frac{1}{2} - 2\frac{1}{4} =$

7) $9\frac{1}{5} - 5\frac{1}{6} =$

8) $14\frac{3}{10} - 13\frac{1}{3} =$

9) $19\frac{2}{3} - 11\frac{5}{8} =$

Multiplying Mixed Numbers

Step-by-step guide:

- ✓ Convert the mixed numbers to improper fractions. (improper fraction is a fraction in which the top number is bigger than bottom number)
- ✓ Multiply fractions and simplify if necessary.

$$a\frac{c}{b} = a + \frac{c}{b} = \frac{ab + c}{b}$$

Examples:

1) Multiply mixed numbers. $3\frac{2}{3} \times 2\frac{1}{2} =$

   Converting mixed numbers to fractions, $3\frac{2}{3} = \frac{11}{3}$ and $2\frac{1}{2} = \frac{5}{2}$.

   $\frac{11}{3} \times \frac{5}{2}$, Applying the fractions formula for multiplication, $\frac{11 \times 5}{3 \times 2} = \frac{55}{6} = 9\frac{1}{6}$

2) Multiply mixed numbers. $4\frac{3}{5} \times 2\frac{1}{3} =$

   Converting mixed numbers to fractions, $\frac{23}{5} \times \frac{7}{3}$, Applying the fractions formula for multiplication, $\frac{23 \times 7}{5 \times 3} = \frac{161}{15} = 10\frac{11}{15}$

✎ *Find the product.*

1) $4\frac{1}{3} \times 2\frac{1}{5} =$

2) $3\frac{1}{2} \times 3\frac{1}{4} =$

3) $5\frac{2}{5} \times 2\frac{1}{3} =$

4) $2\frac{1}{2} \times 1\frac{2}{9} =$

5) $3\frac{4}{7} \times 2\frac{3}{5} =$

6) $7\frac{2}{3} \times 2\frac{2}{3} =$

7) $9\frac{8}{9} \times 8\frac{3}{4} =$

8) $2\frac{4}{7} \times 5\frac{2}{9} =$

9) $5\frac{2}{5} \times 2\frac{3}{5} =$

10) $3\frac{5}{7} \times 3\frac{5}{6} =$

Dividing Mixed Numbers

Step-by-step guide:

✓ Convert the mixed numbers to improper fractions.

✓ Divide fractions and simplify if necessary.

$$a\frac{c}{b} = a + \frac{c}{b} = \frac{ab+c}{b}$$

Examples:

1) Find the quotient. $2\frac{1}{2} \div 1\frac{1}{5} =$

Converting mixed numbers to fractions, $\frac{5}{2} \div \frac{6}{5}$, Applying the fractions formula for multiplication, $\frac{5\times5}{2\times6} = \frac{25}{12} = 2\frac{1}{12}$

2) Find the quotient. $4\frac{3}{4} \div 3\frac{4}{5} =$

Converting mixed numbers to fractions, $\frac{19}{4} \div \frac{19}{5}$, Applying the fractions formula for multiplication, $\frac{19\times5}{4\times19} = \frac{95}{76} = 1\frac{1}{4}$

✎ *Find the quotient.*

1) $1\frac{2}{3} \div 3\frac{1}{3} = \quad \frac{5}{3} \cdot \frac{3}{10} \quad \frac{15}{30} \div \frac{1}{2}$

2) $2\frac{1}{4} \div 1\frac{1}{2} =$

3) $10\frac{1}{2} \div 1\frac{2}{3} =$

4) $3\frac{1}{6} \div 4\frac{2}{3} =$

5) $4\frac{1}{8} \div 2\frac{1}{2} =$

6) $2\frac{1}{10} \div 2\frac{3}{5} =$

7) $1\frac{4}{11} \div 1\frac{1}{4} =$

8) $9\frac{1}{2} \div 9\frac{2}{3} =$

9) $8\frac{3}{4} \div 2\frac{2}{5} -$

10) $12\frac{1}{2} \div 9\frac{1}{3} =$

Answers – Day 3

Adding Mixed Numbers

1) $3\frac{5}{6}$

2) 10

3) $5\frac{1}{2}$

4) $5\frac{3}{4}$

5) $2\frac{11}{14}$

6) $10\frac{1}{6}$

7) $14\frac{1}{4}$

8) $7\frac{5}{24}$

9) $10\frac{29}{33}$

Subtract Mixed Numbers

1) 2

2) 1

3) $3\frac{1}{4}$

4) $\frac{5}{6}$

5) $7\frac{2}{5}$

6) $7\frac{1}{4}$

7) $4\frac{1}{30}$

8) $\frac{29}{30}$

9) $8\frac{1}{24}$

Multiplying Mixed Numbers

1) $9\frac{8}{15}$

2) $11\frac{3}{8}$

3) $12\frac{3}{5}$

4) $3\frac{1}{18}$

5) $9\frac{2}{7}$

6) $20\frac{4}{9}$

7) $86\frac{19}{36}$

8) $13\frac{3}{7}$

9) $14\frac{1}{25}$

10) $14\frac{5}{21}$

Dividing Mixed Numbers

1) $\frac{1}{2}$

2) $1\frac{1}{2}$

3) $6\frac{3}{10}$

4) $\frac{19}{28}$

5) $1\frac{13}{20}$

6) $\frac{21}{26}$

7) $1\frac{1}{11}$

8) $\frac{57}{58}$

9) $3\frac{31}{48}$

10) $1\frac{19}{56}$

Day 4: Decimals

Math Topics that you'll learn today:

- ✓ Comparing Decimals

- ✓ Rounding Decimals

- ✓ Adding and Subtracting Decimals

- ✓ Multiplying and Dividing Decimals

"Do not worry about your difficulties in mathematics. I can assure you mine are still greater." – Albert Einstein

Comparing Decimals

Step-by-step guide:

Decimals: is a fraction written in a special form. For example, instead of writing $\frac{1}{2}$ you can write 0.5.

For comparing decimals:

✓ Compare each digit of two decimals in the same place value.
✓ Start from left. Compare hundreds, tens, ones, tenth, hundredth, etc.
✓ To compare numbers, use these symbols:
- Equal to $=$,   Less than $<$,   Greater than $>$
  Greater than or equal $\geq$,   Less than or equal $\leq$

Examples:

1) Compare 0.20 and 0.02.

   0.20 *is greater than* 0.02, because the tenth place of 0.20 is 2, but the tenth place of 0.02 is zero. Then: $0.20 > 0.02$

2) Compare 0.0210 and 0.110.

   0.0.110 *is greater than* 0.0210, because the tenth place of 0.110 is 1, but the tenth place of 0.0210 is zero. Then: $0.0210 < 0.110$

✍ *Write the correct comparison symbol (>, < or =).*

1) 0.50 ☐ 0.050

2) 0.025 ☐ 0.25

3) 2.060 ☐ 2.07

4) 1.75 ☐ 1.07

5) 4.04 ☐ 0.440

6) 3.05 ☐ 3.5

7) 5.05 ☐ 5.050

8) 1.02 ☐ 1.1

9) 2.45 ☐ 2.125

10) 0.932 ☐ 0.0932

11) 3.15 ☐ 3.150

12) 0.718 ☐ 0.89

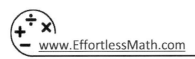

Rounding Decimals

Step-by-step guide:

- ✓ We can round decimals to a certain accuracy or number of decimal places. This is used to make calculation easier to do and results easier to understand, when exact values are not too important.
- ✓ First, you'll need to remember your place values: For example:

$$12.4567$$

1: tens	2: ones	4: tenths
5: hundredths	6: thousandths	7: tens thousandths

- ✓ To round a decimal, find the place value you'll round to.
- ✓ Find the digit to the right of the place value you're rounding to. If it is 5 or bigger, add 1 to the place value you're rounding to and remove all digits on its right side. If the digit to the right of the place value is less than 5, keep the place value and remove all digits on the right.

Examples:

1) Round 2.**1837** to the thousandth place value.

First look at the next place value to the right, (tens thousandths). It's 7 and it is greater than 5. Thus add 1 to the digit in the thousandth place.

Thousandth place is 3. → 3 + 1 = 4, then, the answer is 2.184

2) 2.**1837** rounded to the nearest hundredth.

First look at the next place value to the right of thousandths. It's 3 and it is less than 5, thus remove all the digits to the right. Then, the answer is 2.18.

✎ *Round each decimal to the nearest whole number.*

1) 23.18   3) 14.45   5) 3.95
2) 8.6   4) 7.5   6) 56.7

✎ *Round each decimal to the nearest tenth.*

7) 22.652   9) 47.847   11) 16.184
8) 30.342   10) 82.88   12) 71.79

Adding and Subtracting Decimals

Step-by-step guide:

- ✓ Line up the numbers.
- ✓ Add zeros to have same number of digits for both numbers if necessary.
- ✓ Add or subtract using column addition or subtraction.

Examples:

1) Add. $2.5 + 1.24 =$

First line up the numbers: $\begin{array}{r} 2.5 \\ +\,1.24 \\ \hline \end{array}$ → Add zeros to have same number of digits for both

numbers. $\begin{array}{r} 2.50 \\ +\,1.24 \\ \hline \end{array}$, Start with the hundredths place. $0 + 4 = 4$, $\begin{array}{r} 2.50 \\ +\,1.24 \\ \hline 4 \end{array}$, Continue with tenths

place. $5 + 2 = 7$, $\begin{array}{r} 2.50 \\ +\,1.24 \\ \hline .74 \end{array}$. Add the ones place. $2 + 1 = 3$, $\begin{array}{r} 2.50 \\ +\,1.24 \\ \hline 3.74 \end{array}$

2) Subtract decimals. $4.67 + 2.15 = \begin{array}{r} 4.67 \\ -\,2.15 \\ \hline \end{array}$

Start with the hundredths place. $7 - 5 = 2$, $\begin{array}{r} 4.67 \\ -\,2.15 \\ \hline 2 \end{array}$, continue with tenths place. $6 - 1 = 5$

$\begin{array}{r} 4.67 \\ -\,2.15 \\ \hline .52 \end{array}$, subtract the ones place. $4 - 2 = 2$, $\begin{array}{r} 4.67 \\ -\,2.15 \\ \hline 2.52 \end{array}$.

✍ **Find the sum or difference.**

1) $31.13 - 11.45 =$ 5) $71.47 + 16.25 =$

2) $35.25 + 24.47 =$ 6) $68.99 - 53.61 =$

3) $73.50 + 22.78 =$ 7) $66.24 - 23.11 =$

4) $56.67 - 44.39 =$ 8) $39.75 + 12.85 =$

Multiplying and Dividing Decimals

Step-by-step guide:

For Multiplication:

✓ Ignore the decimal point and set up and multiply the numbers as you do with whole numbers.
Count the total number of decimal places in both of the factors.
Place the decimal point in the product.
For Division:

✓ If the divisor is not a whole number, move decimal point to right to make it a whole number. Do the same for dividend.
✓ Divide similar to whole numbers.

Examples:

1) Find the product. $0.50 \times 0.20 =$

Set up and multiply the numbers as you do with whole numbers. Line up the numbers: $\begin{array}{r} 50 \\ \times\,20 \\ \hline \end{array}$, Start with

the ones place → $50 \times 0 = 0$, $\begin{array}{r} 50 \\ \times\,20 \\ \hline 0 \end{array}$, Continue with other digits → $50 \times 2 = 100$, $\begin{array}{r} 50 \\ \times\,20 \\ \hline 1{,}000 \end{array}$, Count the

total number of decimal places in both of the factors. (4). Then Place the decimal point in the product.

Then: $\begin{array}{r} 0.50 \\ \times\,0.20 \\ \hline 0.1000 \end{array}$ → $0.50 \times 0.20 = 0.1$

2) Find the quotient. $1.20 \div 0.2 =$
The divisor is not a whole number. Multiply it by 10 to get 2. Do the same for the dividend to get 12.
Now, divide: $12 \div 2 = 6$. The answer is 6.

✎ *Find the product and quotient.*

1) $0.5 \times 0.4 =$

2) $2.5 \times 0.2 =$

3) $1.25 \times 0.5 =$

4) $0.75 \times 0.2 =$

5) $1.92 \times 0.8 =$

6) $0.55 \times 0.4 =$

7) $1.67 \div 100 =$

8) $52.2 \div 1{,}000 =$

9) $4.2 \div 2 =$

10) $8.6 \div 0.5 =$

11) $12.6 \div 0.2 =$

12) $16.5 \div 5 =$

Answers – Day 4

Comparing Decimals

1) >
2) <
3) <
4) >
5) >
6) <

7) =
8) <
9) >
10) >
11) =
12) <

Rounding Decimals

1) 23
2) 9
3) 14
4) 8

5) 4
6) 57
7) 22.7
8) 30.3

9) 47.8
10) 82.9
11) 16.2
12) 71.8

Adding and Subtracting Decimals

1) 19.68
2) 59.72
3) 96.28

4) 12.28
5) 87.72
6) 15.38

7) 43.13
8) 52.60

Multiplying and Dividing Decimals

1) 0.20
2) 0.50
3) 0.625
4) 0.15

5) 1.536
6) 0.22
7) 0.0167
8) 0.0522

9) 2.10
10) 17.2
11) 63
12) 3.3

Day 5: Factoring Numbers

Math Topics that you'll learn today:

- ✓ Factoring Numbers

- ✓ Greatest Common Factor

- ✓ Least Common Multiple

"The study of mathematics, like the Nile, begins in minuteness but ends in magnificence."

- Charles Caleb Colton

Factoring Numbers

Step-by-step guide:

   ✓ Factoring numbers means to break the numbers into their prime factors.
   ✓ First few prime numbers: $2, 3, 5, 7, 11, 13, 17, 19$

Examples:

1) List all positive factors of 12.

   Write the upside-down division:
   The second column is the answer.
   Then: $12 = 2 \times 2 \times 3$ or $12 = 2^2 \times 3$

12	2
6	2
3	3
1	

2) List all positive factors of 20.

   Write the upside-down division:
   The second column is the answer.
   Then: $20 = 2 \times 2 \times 5$ or $20 = 2^2 \times 5$

20	2
10	2
5	5
1	

✎ *List all positive factors of each number.*

1) 8	5) 25	9) 42
2) 9	6) 28	10) 48
3) 15	7) 26	11) 50
4) 16	8) 35	12) 36

Greatest Common Factor

Step-by-step guide:

- ✓ List the prime factors of each number.
- ✓ Multiply common prime factors.
- ✓ If there are no common prime factors, the GCF is 1.

Examples:

1) Find the GCF for 10 and 15.

The factors of 10 are: $\{1, 2, 5, 10\}$

The factors of 15 are: $\{1, 3, 5, 15\}$

There is 5 in common,

Then the greatest common factor is: 5.

2) Find the GCF for 8 and 20.

The factors of 8 are: $\{1, 2, 4, 8\}$

The factors of 20 are: $\{1, 2, 4, 5, 10, 20\}$

There is 2 and 4 in common.

Then the greatest common factor is: $2 \times 4 = 8$.

✏️ *Find the GCF for each number pair.*

1) $4, 2$	5) $5, 10$	9) $5, 12$
2) $3, 5$	6) $6, 12$	10) $4, 14$
3) $2, 6$	7) $7, 14$	11) $15, 18$
4) $4, 7$	8) $6, 14$	12) $12, 20$

Least Common Multiple

Step-by-step guide:

- ✓ Least Common Multiple is the smallest multiple that 2 or more numbers have in common.
- ✓ How to find LCM: list out all the multiples of each number and then find the first one they have in common.

Examples:

1) Find the LCM for 3 and 4.

   Multiples of 3: $3, 6, 9, 12, 15, 18, 21, 24$

   Multiples of 4: $4, 8, 12, 16, 20, 24$

   $LCM = 12$

2) Find the LCM for 9 and 12.

   Multiples of 9: $9, 18, 27, 36, 45$

   Multiples of 12: $12, 24, 36, 48$

   $LCM = 36$

✍ Find the LCM for each number pair.

1) 3, 6	5) 6, 18	9) 4, 18
2) 5, 10	6) 10, 12	10) 9, 12
3) 6, 14	7) 4, 12	11) 12, 16
4) 8, 9	8) 5, 15	12) 15, 18

Answers – Day 5

Factoring Numbers

1) 1, 2, 4, 8
2) 1, 3, 9
3) 1, 3, 5, 15
4) 1, 2, 4, 8, 16
5) 1, 5, 25
6) 1, 2, 4, 7, 14, 28

7) 1, 2, 13, 26
8) 1, 5, 7, 35
9) 1, 2, 3, 6, 7, 14, 21, 42
10) 1, 2, 3, 4, 6, 8, 12, 16, 24, 48
11) 1, 2, 5, 10, 25, 50
12) 1, 2, 3, 4, 6, 9, 12, 18, 36

Greatest Common Factor

1) 2
2) 1
3) 2
4) 1
5) 5
6) 12

7) 7
8) 2
9) 1
10) 2
11) 3
12) 4

Least Common Multiple

1) 6
2) 10
3) 42
4) 72
5) 18
6) 60

7) 12
8) 15
9) 36
10) 36
11) 48
12) 90

Day 6: Integers

Math Topics that you'll learn today:

- ✓ Adding and Subtracting Integers

- ✓ Multiplying and Dividing Integers

- ✓ Ordering Integers and Numbers

Without mathematics, there's nothing you can do. Everything around you is mathematics. Everything around you is numbers." - Shakuntala Devi

Adding and Subtracting Integers

Step-by-step guide:

- ✓ Integers includes: zero, counting numbers, and the negative of the counting numbers. $\{\dots, -3, -2, -1, 0, 1, 2, 3, \dots\}$
- ✓ Add a positive integer by moving to the right on the number line.
- ✓ Add a negative integer by moving to the left on the number line.
- ✓ Subtract an integer by adding its opposite.

Examples:

1) Solve. $(-8) - (-5) =$

Keep the first number, and convert the sign of the second number to it's opposite. (change subtraction into addition. Then: $(-8) + 5 = -3$

2) Solve. $10 + (4 - 8) =$

First subtract the numbers in brackets, $4 - 8 = -4$

Then: $10 + (-4) = \rightarrow$ change addition into subtraction: $10 - 4 = 6$

✎ *Find each sum or difference.*

1) $12 + (-5) =$

2) $(-14) + (-18) =$

3) $8 + (-28) =$

4) $43 + (-12) =$

5) $(-7) + (-11) + 4 =$

6) $37 + (-16) + 12 =$

7) $(-12) - (-8) =$

8) $15 - (-20) =$

9) $(-11) - 25 =$

10) $30 - (-16) =$

11) $56 - (45 - 23) =$

12) $15 - (-4) - (-34) =$

Multiplying and Dividing Integers

Step-by-step guide:

Use these rules for multiplying and dividing integers:
- ✓ (negative) × (negative) = positive
- ✓ (negative) ÷ (negative) = positive
- ✓ (negative) × (positive) = negative
- ✓ (negative) ÷ (positive) = negative
- ✓ (positive) × (positive) = positive

Examples:

1) Solve. $(2 - 5) \times (3) =$

First subtract the numbers in brackets, $2 - 5 = -3 \rightarrow (-3) \times (3) =$

Now use this formula: (negative) × (positive) = negative
$(-3) \times (3) = -9$

2) Solve. $(-12) + (48 \div 6) =$

First divided 48 by 6 , the numbers in brackets, $48 \div 6 = 8$

$(-12) + (8) = -12 + 8 = -4$

✍ *Find each product or quotient.*

1) $(-7) \times (-8) =$

2) $(-4) \times 5 =$

3) $5 \times (-11) =$

4) $(-5) \times (-20) =$

5) $-(2) \times (-8) \times 3 =$

6) $(12 - 4) \times (-10) =$

7) $16 \div (-4) =$

8) $(-25) \div (-5) =$

9) $(-40) \div (-8) =$

10) $64 \div (-8) =$

11) $(-49) \div 7 =$

12) $(-112) \div (-4) =$

Ordering Integers and Numbers

Step-by-step guide:

- ✓ When using a number line, numbers increase as you move to the right.
- ✓ When comparing two numbers, think about their position on number line. If one number is on the right side of another number, it is a bigger number. For example, -3 is bigger than -5 because it is on the right side of -5 on number line.

Examples:

1) Order this set of integers from least to greatest. $-2, 1, -5, -1, 2, 4$
The smallest number is -5 and the largest number is 4.

Now compare the integers and order them from greatest to least:
$-5 < -2 < -1 < 1 < 2 < 4$

2) Order each set of integers from greatest to least. $10, -6, -2, 5, -8, 4$
The largest number is 10 and the smallest number is -8.

Now compare the integers and order them from least to greatest:
$10 > 5 > 4 > -2 > -6 > -8$

✍ *Order each set of integers from least to greatest.*

1) $7, -9, -6, -1, 3$ ___, ___, ___, ___, ___, ___
2) $-4, -11, 5, 12, 9$ ___, ___, ___, ___, ___, ___
3) $18, -12, -19, 21, -20$ ___, ___, ___, ___, ___, ___
4) $-15, -25, 18, -7, 32$ ___, ___, ___, ___, ___, ___

✍ *Order each set of integers from greatest to least.*

5) $11, 16, -9, -12, -4$ ___, ___, ___, ___, ___, ___
6) $23, 31, -14, -20, 39$ ___, ___, ___, ___, ___, ___
7) $45, -21, -18, 55, -5$ ___, ___, ___, ___, ___, ___
8) $68, 81, -14, -10, 94$ ___, ___, ___, ___, ___, ___

Answers – Day 6

Adding and Subtracting Integers

1) 7
2) −32
3) −20
4) 31
5) −14
6) 33

7) −4
8) 35
9) −36
10) 46
11) 34
12) 53

Multiplying and Dividing Integers

1) 56
2) −20
3) −55
4) 100
5) 48
6) −80

7) −4
8) 5
9) 5
10) −8
11) −7
12) 28

Ordering Integers and Numbers

1) −9, −6, −1, 3, 7
2) −11, −4, 5, 9, 12
3) −20, −19, −12, 18, 21
4) −25, −15, −7, 18, 32

5) 16, 11, −4, −9, −12
6) 39, 31, 23, −14, −20
7) 55, 45, −5, −18, −21
8) 94, 81, 68, −10, −14

Day 7: Order of Operations

Math Topics that you'll learn today:

- ✓ Order of Operations

- ✓ Integers and Absolute Value

"Sometimes the questions are complicated and the answers are simple." – Dr. Seuss

Order of Operations

Step-by-step guide:

When there is more than one math operation, use PEMDAS:

- ✓ Parentheses

- ✓ Exponents

- ✓ Multiplication and Division (from left to right)

- ✓ Addition and Subtraction (from left to right)

Examples:

1) Solve. $(5 + 7) \div (3^2 \div 3) =$

First simplify inside parentheses: $(12) \div (9 \div 3) = (12) \div (3) =$
Then: $(12) \div (3) = 4$

2) Solve. $(11 \times 5) - (12 - 7) =$

First simplify inside parentheses: $(11 \times 5) - (12 - 7) = (55) - (5) =$

Then: $(55) - (5) = 50$

✎ *Evaluate each expression.*

1) $5 + (4 \times 2) =$

2) $13 - (2 \times 5) =$

3) $(16 \times 2) + 18 =$

4) $(12 - 5) - (4 \times 3) =$

5) $25 + (14 \div 2) =$

6) $(18 \times 5) \div 5 =$

7) $(48 \div 2) \times (-4) =$

8) $(7 \times 5) + (25 - 12) =$

9) $64 + (3 \times 2) + 8 =$

10) $(20 \times 5) \div (4 + 1) =$

11) $(-9) + (12 \times 6) + 15 =$

12) $(7 \times 8) - (56 \div 4) =$

Integers and Absolute Value

Step-by-step guide:

- ✓ To find an absolute value of a number, just find its distance from 0 on number line! For example, the distance of 12 and −12 from zero on number line is 12!

Examples:

1) Solve. $\frac{|-18|}{9} \times |5 - 8| =$

First find $|-18|$, →the absolute value of -18 is 18, then: $|-18| = 18$

$\frac{18}{9} \times |5 - 8| =$

Next, solve $|5 - 8|$, → $|5 - 8| = |-3|$, the absolute value of -3 is 3. $|-3| = 3$

Then: $\frac{18}{9} \times 3 = 2 \times 3 = 6$

2) Solve. $|10 - 5| \times \frac{|-2 \times 6|}{3} =$

First solve $|10 - 5|$, →$|10 - 5| = |5|$, the absolute value of 5 is 5, $|5| = 5$

$5 \times \frac{|-2 \times 6|}{3} =$

Now solve $|-2 \times 6|$, → $|-2 \times 6| = |-12|$, the absolute value of -12 is 12, $|-12| = 12$

Then: $5 \times \frac{12}{3} = 5 \times 4 = 20$

✎ *Evaluate the value.*

1) $8 - |2 - 14| - |-2| =$

2) $|-2| - \frac{|-10|}{2} =$

3) $\frac{|-36|}{6} \times |-6| =$

4) $\frac{|5 \times -3|}{5} \times \frac{|-20|}{4} =$

5) $|2 \times -4| + \frac{|-40|}{5} =$

6) $\frac{|-28|}{4} \times \frac{|-55|}{11} =$

7) $|-12 + 4| \times \frac{|1 \times 5|}{2} =$

8) $\frac{|-10 \times 3|}{2} \times |-12| =$

Answers – Day 7

Order of Operations

1) 13

2) 3

3) 50

4) −5

5) 32

6) 18

7) −96

8) 48

9) 78

10) 20

11) 78

12) 42

Integers and Absolute Value

1) −6

2) −3

3) 36

4) 15

5) 16

6) 35

7) 80

8) 180

Day 8: Ratios

Math Topics that you'll learn today:

- ✓ Simplifying Ratios

- ✓ Proportional Ratios

Mathematics is the door and key to the sciences. – Roger Bacon

Simplifying Ratios

Step-by-step guide:

- ✓ Ratios are used to make comparisons between two numbers.
- ✓ Ratios can be written as a fraction, using the word "to", or with a colon.
- ✓ You can calculate equivalent ratios by multiplying or dividing both sides of the ratio by the same number.

Examples:

1) Simplify. $8 : 4 =$

Both numbers 8 and 4 are divisible by 4 , $\Rightarrow 8 \div 4 = 2, 4 \div 4 = 1,$

Then: $8 : 4 = 2 : 1$

2) Simplify. $\frac{12}{36} =$

Both numbers 12 and 36 are divisible by 12, $\Rightarrow 12 \div 12 = 1, 36 \div 12 = 3,$

Then: $\frac{12}{36} = \frac{1}{3}$

✎ *Reduce each ratio.*

1) $12 : 8 = $ ___ : ___

2) $2 : 20 = $ ___ : ___

3) $3 : 36 = $ ___ : ___

4) $8 : 16 = $ ___ : ___

5) $6 : 100 = $ ___ : ___

6) $10 : 60 = $ ___ : ___

7) $21 : 49 = $ ___ : ___

8) $20 : 40 = $ ___ : ___

9) $10 : 50 = $ ___ : ___

10) $14 : 18 = $ ___ : ___

11) $45 : 27 = $ ___ : ___

12) $49 : 21 = $ ___ : ___

Proportional Ratios

Step-by-step guide:

- ✓ A proportion means that two ratios are equal. It can be written in two ways:
  $\frac{a}{b} = \frac{c}{d}$, $a : b = c : d$

- ✓ The proportion $\frac{a}{b} = \frac{c}{d}$ can be written as: $a \times d = c \times b$

Examples:

1) Solve this proportion for x. $\frac{4}{8} = \frac{5}{x}$

   Use cross multiplication: $\frac{4}{8} = \frac{5}{x} \Rightarrow 4 \times x = 5 \times 8 \Rightarrow 4x = 40$

   Divide to find x: $\quad x = \frac{40}{4} \Rightarrow x = 10$

2) If a box contains red and blue balls in ratio of $2 : 3$ red to blue, how many red balls are there if 90 blue balls are in the box?

   Write a proportion and solve. $\frac{2}{3} = \frac{x}{90}$

   Use cross multiplication: $2 \times 90 = 3 \times x \Rightarrow 180 = 3x$

   Divide to find x: $\qquad x = \frac{180}{3} \Rightarrow x = 60$

✎ *Solve each proportion.*

1) $\frac{2}{5} = \frac{14}{x}$, $x = $ ____

2) $\frac{1}{6} = \frac{7}{x}$, $x = $ ____

3) $\frac{3}{5} = \frac{27}{x}$, $x = $ ____

4) $\frac{1}{5} = \frac{x}{80}$, $x = $ ____

5) $\frac{3}{7} = \frac{x}{63}$, $x = $ ____

6) $\frac{1}{4} = \frac{13}{x}$, $x = $ ____

7) $\frac{7}{9} = \frac{56}{x}$, $x = $ ____

8) $\frac{6}{11} = \frac{42}{x}$, $x = $ ____

9) $\frac{4}{7} = \frac{x}{77}$, $x = $ ____

10) $\frac{5}{13} = \frac{x}{143}$, $x = $ ____

11) $\frac{7}{19} = \frac{x}{209}$, $x = $ ____

12) $\frac{3}{13} = \frac{x}{195}$, $x = $ ____

Answers – Day 8

Simplifying Ratios

1) 3 : 2	7) 3 : 7
2) 1 : 10	8) 1 : 2
3) 1 : 12	9) 1 : 5
4) 1 : 2	10) 7 : 9
5) 3 : 50	11) 5 : 3
6) 1 : 6	12) 7 : 3

Proportional Ratios

1) 35	7) 72
2) 42	8) 77
3) 45	9) 44
4) 16	10) 55
5) 27	11) 77
6) 52	12) 45

Day 9: Similarity and Proportions

Math Topics that you'll learn today:

- ✓ Create a Proportion

- ✓ Similarity and Ratios

- ✓ Simple Interest

Mathematics - the unshaken Foundation of Sciences, and the plentiful Fountain of Advantage to human affairs. -

Isaac Barrow

Create a Proportion

Step-by-step guide:

✓ A proportion contains two equal fractions! A proportion simply means that two fractions are equal.

✓ To create a proportion, simply find (or create) two equal fractions.

Examples:

1) Express ratios as a Proportion.

120 miles on 4 gallons of gas, how many miles on 1 gallon of gas?

First create a fraction: $\dfrac{120 \ miles}{4 \ gallons}$, and divide: $120 \div 4 = 30$

Then: 30 miles per gallon

2) State if this pair of ratios form a proportion. $\dfrac{3}{5} \ and \ \dfrac{24}{45}$

Use cross multiplication: $\dfrac{3}{5} = \dfrac{24}{45} \rightarrow 3 \times 45 = 5 \times 24 \rightarrow 135 = 120$, which is not correct. Therefore, this pair of ratios doesn't form a proportion.

✎ *State if each pair of ratios form a proportion.*

1) $\dfrac{3}{10} \ and \ \dfrac{9}{30}$ 5) $\dfrac{2}{5} \ and \ \dfrac{16}{45}$ 9) $\dfrac{6}{17} \ and \ \dfrac{36}{85}$

2) $\dfrac{1}{2} \ and \ \dfrac{16}{32}$ 6) $\dfrac{4}{9} \ and \ \dfrac{40}{81}$ 10) $\dfrac{2}{7} \ and \ \dfrac{24}{86}$

3) $\dfrac{5}{6} \ and \ \dfrac{35}{42}$ 7) $\dfrac{6}{11} \ and \ \dfrac{42}{77}$ 11) $\dfrac{12}{19} \ and \ \dfrac{156}{247}$

4) $\dfrac{3}{7} \ and \ \dfrac{27}{72}$ 8) $\dfrac{1}{6} \ and \ \dfrac{8}{48}$ 12) $\dfrac{13}{21} \ and \ \dfrac{182}{294}$

Similarity and Ratios

Step-by-step guide:

✓ Two or more figures are similar if the corresponding corresponding sides are in proportion.

Examples:

1) A girl 160 cm tall, stands 360 cm from a lamp post at night. Her shadow from the light is 90 cm long. How high is the lamp post?

Write the proportion and solve for missing side.

$$\frac{\text{Smaller triangle height}}{\text{Smaller triangle base}} = \frac{\text{Bigger triangle height}}{\text{Bigger triangle base}}$$

$$\Rightarrow \frac{90cm}{160cm} = \frac{90+360cm}{x} \Rightarrow 90x = 160 \times 450 \Rightarrow x = 800 \ cm$$

2) A tree 32 $feet$ tall casts a shadow 12 $feet$ long. Jack is 6 $feet$ tall. How long is Jack's shadow?

Write a proportion and solve for the missing number.

$$\frac{32}{12} = \frac{6}{x} \rightarrow 32x = 6 \times 12$$

$$32x = 72 \rightarrow x = \frac{72}{32} = 2.25$$

✐ Solve.

1) Two rectangles are similar. The first is 6 $feet$ wide and 20 $feet$ long. The second is 15 $feet$ wide. What is the length of the second rectangle? _____

2) Two rectangles are similar. One is 2.5 $meters$ by 9 $meters$. The longer side of the second rectangle is 22.5 $meters$. What is the other side of the second rectangle? _____

3) A building casts a shadow 24 ft long. At the same time a girl 5 ft tall casts a shadow 2 ft long. How tall is the building? _____

4) The scale of a map of Texas is 2 $inches$: 45 $miles$. If you measure the distance from Dallas to Martin County as 14.4 $inches$, approximately how far is Martin County from Dallas? _____

Simple Interest

Step-by-step guide:

✓ Simple Interest: The charge for borrowing money or the return for lending it. To solve a simple interest problem, use this formula:

Interest = principal x rate x time ⟹ $I = p \times r \times t$

Examples:

1) Find simple interest for $450 investment at 7% for 8 years.

Use Interest formula: $I = prt$

$p = \$450$, r = 7% = $\frac{7}{100}$ = 0.07 and $t = 8$

Then: $I = 450 \times 0.07 \times 8 = \$252$

2) Find simple interest for $5,200 at 4% for 3 years.

Use Interest formula: $I = prt$

$p = \$5,200$, r = 4% = $\frac{4}{100}$ = 0.04 and $t = 3$

Then: $I = 5,200 \times 0.04 \times 3 = \$624$

✎ *Determine the simple interest for these loans.*

1) $1,300 at 5% for 6 years. $ _____

2) $5,400 at 3.5% for 6 months. $ _____

3) $600 at 4% for 9 months. $ _____

4) $24,000 at 5.5% for 5 years. $ _____

5) $15,600 at 3% for 2 years. $ _____

6) $1,200 at 5.5% for 4 years. $ _____

7) $1,600 at 4.5% for 9 months. $ _____

8) $12,000 at 2.2% for 5 years. $ _____

Answers – Day 9

Create a Proportion

1) Yes
2) Yes
3) Yes
4) No
5) No
6) No

7) Yes
8) Yes
9) No
10) No
11) Yes
12) Yes

Similarity and ratios

1) 50 feet
2) 6.25 meters
3) 60 feet
4) 324 miles

Simple Interest

1) $390.00
2) $94.50
3) $18.00
4) $6,600.00

5) $936.00
6) $264.00
7) $54
8) $1,320.00

Day 10: Percentage

Math Topics that you'll learn today:

✓ Percentage Calculations

✓ Percent Problems

Mathematics is no more computation than typing is literature.

– John Allen Paulos

Percentage Calculations

Step-by-step guide:

✓ Percent is a ratio of a number and 100. It always has the same denominator, 100. Percent symbol is %.

✓ Percent is another way to write decimals or fractions. For example:
$$40\% = 0.40 = \frac{40}{100} = \frac{2}{5}$$

✓ Use the following formula to find part, whole, or percent:
$$\text{part} = \frac{\text{percent}}{100} \times \text{whole}$$

Examples:

1) What is 10% of 45? Use the following formula: $\text{part} = \frac{\text{percent}}{100} \times \text{whole}$

$$\text{part} = \frac{10}{100} \times 45 \;\rightarrow\; \text{part} = \frac{1}{10} \times 45 \rightarrow \text{part} = \frac{45}{10} \rightarrow \text{part} = 4.5$$

2) What is 15% of 24? Use the percent formula: $\text{part} = \frac{\text{percent}}{100} \times \text{whole}$

$$\text{part} = \frac{15}{100} \times 24 \;\rightarrow\; \text{part} = \frac{360}{100} \rightarrow \text{part} = 3.6$$

✎ *Calculate the given percent of each value.*

1) 2% of 50 = ____

2) 10% of 30 = ____

3) 20% of 25 = ____

4) 50% of 80 = ____

5) 40% of 200 = ____

6) 20% of 45 = ____

7) 35% of 20 = ____

8) 12% of 400 = ____

9) 40% of 90 = ____

10) 25% of 812 = ____

11) 32% of 600 = ____

12) 87% of 500 = ____

Percent Problems

Step-by-step guide:

   ✓ In each percent problem, we are looking for the base, or part or the percent.
   ✓ Use the following equations to find each missing section.
      ○ Base = Part ÷ Percent
      ○ Part = Percent × Base
      ○ Percent = Part ÷ Base

Examples:

1) 1.2 is what percent of 24?

   In this problem, we are looking for the percent. Use the following equation:
$$Percent = Part \div Base \rightarrow Percent = 1.2 \div 24 = 0.05 = 5\%$$

2) 20 is 5% of what number?

   Use the following formula: $Base = Part \div Percent \rightarrow Base = 20 \div 0.05 = 400$
   20 is 5% of 400.

✎ Solve each problem.

1) 20 is what percent of 50? ____%

2) 18 is what percent of 90? ____%

3) 12 is what percent of 15? ____%

4) 16 is what percent of 200? ____%

5) 24 is what percent of 800? ____%

6) 48 is what percent of 400? ____%

7) 90 is 12 percent of what number? ____

8) 24 is 8 percent of what? ____

9) 60 is 15 percent of what number? ____

10) 42 is 12 percent of what? ____

11) 11 is 25 percent of what? ____

12) 8 is 12.5 percent of what? ____

Answers – Day 10

Percentage Calculations

1) 1
2) 3
3) 5
4) 40
5) 80
6) 9

7) 7
8) 48
9) 36
10) 203
11) 192
12) 435

Percent Problems

1) 40%
2) 20%
3) 80%
4) 8%
5) 3%
6) 12%

7) 750
8) 300
9) 400
10) 350
11) 44
12) 64

Day 11: Percent of Change

Math Topics that you'll learn today:

- ✓ Percent of Increase and Decrease

- ✓ Discount, Tax and Tip

Mathematics is a great motivator for all humans. Because its career starts with zero and it never end (infinity).

Percent of Increase and Decrease

Step-by-step guide:

To find the percentage of increase or decrease:
- ✓ New Number – Original Number
- ✓ The result ÷ Original Number × 100
- ✓ If your answer is a negative number, then this is a percentage decrease. If it is positive, then this is a percent of increase.

Examples:

1) Increased by 50%, the numbers 84 becomes:

First find 50% of 84 → $\frac{50}{100} \times 84 = \frac{50 \times 84}{100} = 42$

Then: $84 + 42 = 126$

2) The price of a shirt increases from \$10 to \$14. What is the percent increase?

First: $14 - 10 = 4$

4 is the result. Then: $4 \div 10 = \frac{4}{10} = 0.4 = 40\%$

✎ *Solve each percent of change word problem.*

1) Bob got a raise, and his hourly wage increased from \$12 to \$15. What is the percent increase? _____ %

2) The price of a pair of shoes increases from \$20 to \$32. What is the percent increase? ____ %

3) At a coffeeshop, the price of a cup of coffee increased from \$1.20 to \$1.44. What is the percent increase in the cost of the coffee? _____ %

4) 6 cm are cut from a 24 cm board. What is the percent decrease in length? _____ %

5) In a class, the number of students has been increased from 18 to 27. What is the percent increase? _____ %

6) The price of gasoline rose from \$2.40 to \$2.76 in one month. By what percent did the gas price rise? _____ %

7) A shirt was originally priced at \$48. It went on sale for \$38.40. What was the percent that the shirt was discounted? _____ %

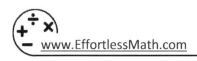

www.EffortlessMath.com

Discount, Tax and Tip

Step-by-step guide:

- ✓ Discount = Multiply the regular price by the rate of discount
- ✓ Selling price = original price – discount
- ✓ Tax: To find tax, multiply the tax rate to the taxable amount (income, property value, etc.)
- ✓ To find tip, multiply the rate to the selling price.

Examples:

1) With an 10% discount, Ella was able to save $20 on a dress. What was the original price of the dress?

$10\% \ of \ x = \ 20, \frac{10}{100} \times x = \ 20, x = \frac{100 \times 20}{10} = 200$

2) Sophia purchased a sofa for $530.40. The sofa is regularly priced at $624. What was the percent discount Sophia received on the sofa?

Use this formula: $percent = Part \div base = 530.40 \div 624 = 0.85 = 85\%$

Therefore, the discount is: $100\% - 85\% = 15\%$

✎ *Find the selling price of each item.*

1) Original price of a computer: $500

  Tax: 6%, Selling price: $_____

2) Original price of a laptop: $350

  Tax: 8%, Selling price: $_____

3) Original price of a sofa: $800

  Tax: 7%, Selling price: $_____

4) Original price of a car: $18,500

  Tax: 8.5%, Selling price: $_____

5) Original price of a Table: $250

  Tax: 5%, Selling price: $_____

6) Original price of a house: $250,000

  Tax: 6.5% Selling price: $_____

7) Original price of a tablet: $400

  Discount: 20%, Selling price: $_____

8) Original price of a chair: $150

  Discount: 15%, Selling price: $_____

9) Original price of a book: $50

  Discount: 25%, Selling price: $_____

10) Original price of a cellphone: $500

  Discount: 10%, Selling price: $_____

Answers – Day 11

Percent of Increase and Decrease

1) 25%

2) 60%

3) 20%

4) 25%

5) 50%

6) 15%

7) 20%

Markup, Discount, and Tip

1) $530.00

2) $378.00

3) $856.00

4) $20,072.50

5) $262.50

6) $266,250

7) $320.00

8) $127.50

9) $37.50

10) $450.00

Day 12: Exponents and Variables

Math Topics that you'll learn today:

- ✓ Multiplication Property of Exponents

- ✓ Division Property of Exponents

- ✓ Powers of Products and Quotients

Multiplication Property of Exponents

Step-by-step guide:

✓ Exponents are shorthand for repeated multiplication of the same number by itself. For example, instead of 2×2, we can write 2^2. For $3 \times 3 \times 3 \times 3$, we can write 3^4

✓ In algebra, a variable is a letter used to stand for a number. The most common letters are: $x, y, z, a, b, c, m, $ and n.

✓ Exponent's rules: $x^a \times x^b = x^{a+b}$, $\frac{x^a}{x^b} = x^{a-b}$

$$(x^a)^b = x^{a \times b}, \qquad (xy)^a = x^a \times y^a, (\frac{a}{b})^c = \frac{a^c}{b^c}$$

Examples:

1) Multiply. $-2x^5 \times 7x^3 =$

Use Exponent's rules: $x^a \times x^b = x^{a+b} \rightarrow x^5 \times x^3 = x^{5+3} = x^8$

Then: $-2x^5 \times 7x^3 = -14x^8$

2) Multiply. $(x^2y^4)^3 =$

Use Exponent's rules: $(x^a)^b = x^{a \times b}$. Then: $(x^2y^4)^3 = x^{2 \times 3}y^{4 \times 3} = x^6y^{12}$

✍ *Simplify and write the answer in exponential form.*

1) $x^4 \times 3x =$

2) $x \times 2x^2 =$

3) $5x^4 \times 5x^4 =$

4) $2yx^2 \times 2x =$

5) $3x^4 \times y^2x^4 =$

6) $y^2x^3 \times y^5x^2 =$

7) $4yx^3 \times 2x^2y^3 =$

8) $6x^2 \times 6x^3y^4 =$

9) $3x^4y^5 \times 7x^2y^3 =$

10) $7x^2y^5 \times 9xy^3 =$

11) $7xy^4 \times 4x^3y^3 =$

12) $3x^5y^3 \times 8x^2y^3 =$

Division Property of Exponents

Step-by-step guide:

✓ For division of exponents use these formulas: $\frac{x^a}{x^b} = x^{a-b}$, $x \neq 0$

$$\frac{x^a}{x^b} = \frac{1}{x^{b-a}} , x \neq 0, \qquad \frac{1}{x^b} = x^{-b}$$

Examples:

1) Simplify. $\frac{4x^3y}{36x^2y^3} =$

First cancel the common factor: $4 \rightarrow \frac{4x^3y}{36x^2y^3} = \frac{x^3y}{9x^2y^3}$

Use Exponent's rules: $\frac{x^a}{x^b} = x^{a-b} \rightarrow \frac{x^3}{x^2} = x^{3-2} = x$

Then: $\frac{4x^3y}{36x^2y^3} = \frac{xy}{9y^3} \rightarrow$ now cancel the common factor: $y \rightarrow \frac{xy}{9y^3} = \frac{x}{9y^2}$

2) Divide. $\frac{2x^{-5}}{9x^{-2}} =$

Use Exponent's rules: $\frac{x^a}{x^b} = \frac{1}{x^{b-a}} \rightarrow \frac{x^{-5}}{x^{-2}} = \frac{1}{x^{-2-(-5)}} = \frac{1}{x^{-2+5}} = \frac{1}{x^3}$

Then: $\frac{2x^{-5}}{9x^{-2}} = \frac{2}{9x^3}$

✍ Simplify.

1) $\frac{3^4 \times 3^7}{3^2 \times 3^8} =$

2) $\frac{5x}{10x^3} =$

3) $\frac{3x^3}{2x^5} =$

4) $\frac{12x^3}{14x^6} =$

5) $\frac{12x^3}{9y^8} =$

6) $\frac{25xy^4}{5x^6y^2} =$

7) $\frac{2x^4}{7x} =$

8) $\frac{16x^2y^8}{4x^3} =$

9) $\frac{12x^4}{15x^7y^9} =$

10) $\frac{12yx^4}{10yx^8} =$

11) $\frac{16x^4y}{9x^8y^2} =$

12) $\frac{5x^8}{20x^8} =$

Powers of Products and Quotients

Step-by-step guide:

✓ For any nonzero numbers a and b and any integer x, $(ab)^x = a^x \times b^x$.

Example:

1) Simplify. $(3x^5y^4)^2 =$

Use Exponent's rules: $(x^a)^b = x^{a \times b}$

$(3x^5y^4)^2 = (3)^2(x^5)^2(y^4)^2 = 9x^{5 \times 2}y^{4 \times 2} = 9x^{10}y^8$

2) Simplify. $(\frac{2x}{3x^2})^2 =$

First cancel the common factor: $x \rightarrow (\frac{2x}{3x^2})^2 = (\frac{2}{3x})^2$

Use Exponent's rules: $(\frac{a}{b})^c = \frac{a^c}{b^c}$

Then: $(\frac{2}{3x})^2 = \frac{2^2}{(3x)^2} = \frac{4}{9x^2}$

✎ *Simplify.*

1) $(4x^3x^3)^2 =$

2) $(3x^3 \times 5x)^2 =$

3) $(10x^{11}y^3)^2 =$

4) $(9x^{7}{}^{5})^2 =$

5) $(4x^4y^6)^5 =$

6) $(3x \times 4y^3)^2 =$

7) $(\frac{5x}{x^2})^2 =$

8) $(\frac{x^4y^4}{x^2y^2})^3 =$

9) $(\frac{25x}{5x^6})^2 =$

10) $(\frac{x^8}{x^6y^2})^2 =$

11) $(\frac{xy^2}{x^3y^3})^{-2} =$

12) $(\frac{2xy^4}{x^3})^2 =$

Answers – Day 12

Multiplication Property of Exponents

1) $3x^5$
2) $2x^3$
3) $25x^8$
4) $4x^3y$
5) $3x^8y^2$
6) x^5y^7

7) $8x^5y^4$
8) $36x^5y^4$
9) $21x^6y^8$
10) $63x^3y^8$
11) $28x^4y^7$
12) $24x^7y^6$

Division Property of Exponents

1) 3
2) $\dfrac{1}{2x^2}$
3) $\dfrac{3}{2x^2}$
4) $\dfrac{6}{7x^3}$
5) $\dfrac{4x^3}{3y^8}$
6) $\dfrac{5y^2}{x^5}$

7) $\dfrac{2x^3}{7}$
8) $\dfrac{4y^8}{x}$
9) $\dfrac{4}{5x^3y^9}$
10) $\dfrac{6}{5x^4}$
11) $\dfrac{16}{9x^4y}$
12) $\dfrac{1}{4}$

Powers of Products and Quotients

1) $16x^{12}$
2) $225x^8$
3) $100x^{22}y^6$
4) $81x^{14}y^{10}$
5) $1,024x^{20}y^{30}$
6) $144x^2y^6$
7) $\dfrac{25}{x^2}$

8) x^6y^6
9) $\dfrac{25}{x^{10}}$
10) $\dfrac{x^4}{y^4}$
11) x^4y^2
12) $\dfrac{4y^8}{x^4}$

Day 13: Exponents and Roots

Math Topics that you'll learn today:

- ✓ Zero and Negative Exponents

- ✓ Negative Exponents and Negative Bases

- ✓ Scientific Notation

- ✓ Square Roots

Mathematics is an independent world created out of pure intelligence.

~ William Woods Worth

Zero and Negative Exponents

Step-by-step guide:

✓ A negative exponent simply means that the base is on the wrong side of the fraction line, so you need to flip the base to the other side. For instance, "x^{-2}" (pronounced as "ecks to the minus two") just means "x^2" but underneath, as in $\frac{1}{x^2}$.

Example:

1) Evaluate. $\left(\frac{4}{9}\right)^{-2} =$

Use Exponent's rules: $\frac{1}{b} = x^{-b} \rightarrow \left(\frac{4}{9}\right)^{-2} = \frac{1}{\left(\frac{4}{9}\right)^2} = \frac{1}{\frac{4^2}{9^2}}$

Now use fraction rule: $\frac{1}{\frac{b}{c}} = \frac{c}{b} \rightarrow \frac{1}{\frac{4^2}{9^2}} = \frac{9^2}{4^2} = \frac{81}{16}$

2) Evaluate. $\left(\frac{5}{6}\right)^{-3} =$

Use Exponent's rules: $\frac{1}{x^b} = x^{-b} \rightarrow \left(\frac{5}{6}\right)^{-3} = \frac{1}{\left(\frac{5}{6}\right)^3} = \frac{1}{\frac{5^3}{6^3}}$

Now use fraction rule: $\frac{1}{\frac{b}{c}} = \frac{c}{b} \rightarrow \frac{1}{\frac{5^3}{6^3}} = \frac{6^3}{5^3} = \frac{216}{125}$

✎ *Evaluate the following expressions.*

1) $2^{-3} =$

2) $3^{-3} =$

3) $7^{-3} =$

4) $6^{-3} =$

5) $8^{-3} =$

6) $9^{-2} =$

7) $10^{-3} =$

8) $10^{-9} =$

9) $\left(\frac{1}{2}\right)^{-1}$

10) $\left(\frac{1}{2}\right)^{-2} =$

11) $\left(\frac{1}{3}\right)^{-2} =$

12) $\left(\frac{2}{3}\right)^{-2} =$

Negative Exponents and Negative Bases

Step-by-step guide:

✓ Make the power positive. A negative exponent is the reciprocal of that number with a positive exponent.
✓ The parenthesis is important!
✓ 5^{-2} is not the same as $(-5)^{-2}$

$$(-5)^{-2} = -\frac{1}{5^2} \text{ and } (-5)^{-2} = +\frac{1}{5^2}$$

Example:

1) Simplify. $\left(\frac{3a}{2c}\right)^{-2} =$

Use Exponent's rules: $\frac{1}{x^b} = x^{-b} \rightarrow \left(\frac{3a}{2c}\right)^{-2} = \frac{1}{\left(\frac{3a}{2c}\right)^2} = \frac{1}{\frac{3^2 a^2}{2^2 c^2}}$

Now use fraction rule: $\frac{1}{\frac{b}{c}} = \frac{c}{b} \rightarrow \frac{1}{\frac{3^2 a^2}{2^2 c^2}} = \frac{2^2 c^2}{3^2 a^2}$

Then: $\frac{2^2 c^2}{3^2 a^2} = \frac{4c^2}{9a^2}$

2) Simplify. $\left(-\frac{5x}{3yz}\right)^{-3} =$

Use Exponent's rules: $\frac{1}{x^b} = x^{-b} \rightarrow \left(-\frac{5x}{3yz}\right)^{-3} = \frac{1}{\left(-\frac{5x}{3yz}\right)^3} = \frac{1}{-\frac{5^3 x^3}{3^3 y^3 z^3}}$

Now use fraction rule: $\frac{1}{\frac{b}{c}} = \frac{c}{b} \rightarrow \frac{1}{-\frac{5^3 x^3}{3^3 y^3 z^3}} = -\frac{3^3 y^3 z^3}{5^3 x^3} = -\frac{27 y^3 z^3}{125 x^3}$

✎ **Simplify.**

1) $-5x^{-2}y^{-3} =$

2) $20x^{-4}y^{-1} =$

3) $14a^{-6}b^{-7} =$

4) $-12x^2 y^{-3} =$

5) $-\frac{25}{x^{-6}} =$

6) $\frac{7b}{-9c^{-4}} =$

7) $\frac{7ab}{a^{-3}b^{-1}} =$

8) $-\frac{5n^{-2}}{10p^{-3}} =$

9) $\frac{4ab^{-2}}{-3c^{-2}} =$

10) $\left(\frac{3a}{2c}\right)^{-2} =$

11) $\left(-\frac{5x}{3yz}\right)^{-3} =$

12) $\frac{1ab^{-2}}{-3c^{-2}} =$

13) $\left(-\frac{x^3}{x^4}\right)^{-2} =$

Scientific Notation

Step-by-step guide:

- ✓ It is used to write very big or very small numbers in decimal form.
- ✓ In scientific notation all numbers are written in the form of:

$$m \times 10^n$$

Decimal notation	Scientific notation
5	5×10^0
$-25,000$	-2.5×10^4
0.5	5×10^{-1}
2,122.456	$2,122456 \times 10^3$

Example:

1) Write **0.00012** in scientific notation.

First, move the decimal point to the right so that you have a number that is between 1 and 10. Then: $N = 1.2$

Second, determine how many places the decimal moved in step 1 by the power of 10. Then: $10^{-4} \rightarrow$ When the decimal moved to the right, the exponent is negative.

Then: $0.00012 = 1.2 \times 10^{-4}$

2) Write **8.3×10^{-5}** in standard notation.

$10^{-5} \rightarrow$ When the decimal moved to the right, the exponent is negative.

Then: $8.3 \times 10^{-5} = 0.000083$

✎ *Write each number in scientific notation.*

1) $0.000325 =$

2) $0.00023 =$

3) $56,000,000 =$

4) $21,000 =$

✎ *Write each number in standard notation.*

5) $3 \times 10^{-1} =$

6) $5 \times 10^{-2} =$

7) $1.2 \times 10^3 =$

8) $2 \times 10^{-4} =$

Square Roots

Step-by-step guide:

✓ A square root of x is a number r whose square is: $r^2 = x$

r is a square root of x.

Example:

1) Find the square root of $\sqrt{225}$.

First factor the number: $225 = 15^2$, Then: $\sqrt{225} = \sqrt{15^2}$

Now use radical rule: $\sqrt[n]{a^n} = a$

Then: $\sqrt{15^2} = 15$

2) Evaluate. $\sqrt{4} \times \sqrt{16} =$

First factor the numbers: $4 = 2^2$ and $16 = 4^2$

Then: $\sqrt{4} \times \sqrt{16} = \sqrt{2^2} \times \sqrt{4^2}$

Now use radical rule: $\sqrt[n]{a^n} = a$, Then: $\sqrt{2^2} \times \sqrt{4^2} = 2 \times 4 = 8$

✏ *Evaluate.*

1) $\sqrt{4} \times \sqrt{9} = $ _____

2) $\sqrt{25} \times \sqrt{64} = $ _____

3) $\sqrt{2} \times \sqrt{8} = $ _____

4) $\sqrt{6} \times \sqrt{6} = $ _____

5) $\sqrt{5} \times \sqrt{5} = $ _____

6) $\sqrt{8} \times \sqrt{8} = $ _____

7) $\sqrt{2} + \sqrt{2} = $ _____

8) $\sqrt{8} + \sqrt{8} = $ _____

9) $4\sqrt{5} - 2\sqrt{5} = $ _____

10) $3\sqrt{3} \times 2\sqrt{3} = $ _____

11) $8\sqrt{2} \times 2\sqrt{2} = $ _____

12) $6\sqrt{3} - \sqrt{12} = $ _____

Answers – Day 13

Zero and Negative Exponents

1) $\frac{1}{8}$

2) $\frac{1}{27}$

3) $\frac{1}{343}$

4) $\frac{1}{216}$

5) $\frac{1}{512}$

6) $\frac{1}{81}$

7) $\frac{1}{1,000}$

8) $\frac{1}{1,000,000,000}$

9) 2

10) 4

11) 9

12) $\frac{9}{4}$

Negative Exponents and Negative Bases

1) $-\frac{5}{x^2 y^3}$

2) $\frac{20}{x^4 y}$

3) $\frac{14}{a^6 b^7}$

4) $-\frac{12x^2}{y^3}$

5) $-25x^6$

6) $-\frac{7bc^4}{9}$

7) $7a^4 b^2$

8) $-\frac{p^3}{2n^2}$

9) $-\frac{4ac^2}{3b^2}$

10) $\frac{4c^2}{9a^2}$

11) $-\frac{27y^3 z^3}{125x^3}$

12) $-\frac{4ac^2}{3b^2}$

13) x^2

Scientific Notation

1) 3.25×10^{-4}

2) 2.3×10^{-4}

3) 5.6×10^7

4) 2.1×10^4

5) 0.3

6) 0.05

7) $1,200$

8) 0.0002

Square Roots

1) 6

2) 40

3) 4

4) 6

5) 5

6) 8

7) $2\sqrt{2}$

8) $2\sqrt{8}$

9) $2\sqrt{5}$

10) 18

11) 32

12) $4\sqrt{3}$

Day 14: Expressions and Variables

Math Topics that you'll learn today:

- ✓ Simplifying Variable Expressions

- ✓ Simplifying Polynomial Expressions

- ✓ Translate Phrases into an Algebraic Statement

Mathematics is, as it were, a sensuous logic, and relates to philosophy as do the arts, music, and plastic art to poetry. – K.

Shegel

Simplifying Variable Expressions

Step-by-step guide:

- ✓ In algebra, a variable is a letter used to stand for a number. The most common letters are: $x, y, z, a, b, c, m, and\ n$.
- ✓ algebraic expression is an expression contains integers, variables, and the math operations such as addition, subtraction, multiplication, division, etc.
- ✓ In an expression, we can combine "like" terms. (values with same variable and same power)

Examples:

1) Simplify this expression. $(10x + 2x + 3) =$?
   Combine like terms. Then: $(10x + 2x + 3) = 12x + 3$ (remember you cannot combine variables and numbers.

2) Simplify this expression. $12 - 3x^2 + 9x + 5x^2 =$?
   Combine "like" terms: $-3x^2 + 5x^2 = 2x^2$

   Then: $12 - 3x^2 + 9x + 5x^2 = 12 + 2x^2 + 9x$. Write in standard form (biggest powers first): $2x^2 + 9x + 12$

Simplify each expression.

1) $(2x + x + 3 + 24) =$

2) $(-28x - 20x + 24) =$

3) $7x + 3 - 3x =$

4) $-2 - x^2 - 6x^2 =$

5) $3 + 10x^2 + 2 =$

6) $8x^2 + 6x + 7x^2 =$

7) $5x^2 - 12x^2 + 8x =$

8) $2x^2 - 2x - x =$

9) $4x + (12 - 30x) =$

10) $10x + (80x - 48) =$

11) $(-18x - 54) - 5 =$

12) $2x^2 + (-8x) =$

Simplifying Polynomial Expressions

Step-by-step guide:

- ✓ In mathematics, a polynomial is an expression consisting of variables and coefficients that involves only the operations of addition, subtraction, multiplication, and non-negative integer exponents of variables.

$$P(x) = a_n x^n + a_{n-1} x^{n-1} + \ldots + a_2 x^2 + a_1 x + a_0$$

Examples:

1) Simplify this Polynomial Expressions. $4x^2 - 5x^3 + 15x^4 - 12x^3 =$
Combine "like" terms: $-5x^3 - 12x^3 = -17x^3$
Then: $4x^2 - 5x^3 + 15x^4 - 12x^3 = 4x^2 - 17x^3 + 15x^4$
Then write in standard form: $4x^2 - 17x^3 + 15x^4 = 15x^4 - 17x^3 + 4x^2$

2) Simplify this expression. $(2x^2 - x^4) - (4x^4 - x^2) =$
First use distributive property: → multiply $(-)$ into $(4x^4 - x^2)$
$(2x^2 - x^4) - (4x^4 - x^2) = 2x^2 - x^4 - 4x^4 + x^2$
Then combine "like" terms: $2x^2 - x^4 - 4x^4 + x^2 = 3x^2 - 5x^4$
And write in standard form: $3x^2 - 5x^4 = -5x^4 + 3x^2$

✍ *Simplify each polynomial.*

1) $(2x^3 + 5x^2) - (12x + 2x^2) = $ _____

2) $(2x^5 + 2x^3) - (7x^3 + 6x^2) = $ _____

3) $(12x^4 + 4x^2) - (2x^2 - 6x^4) = $ _____

4) $14x - 3x^2 - 2(6x^2 + 6x^3) = $ _____

5) $(5x^3 - 3) + 5(2x^2 - 3x^3) = $ _____

6) $(4x^3 - 2x) - 2(4x^3 - 2x^4) = $ _____

7) $2(4x - 3x^3) - 3(3x^3 + 4x^2) - $ _____

8) $(2x^2 - 2x) - (2x^3 + 5x^2) = $ _____

Translate Phrases into an Algebraic Statement

Step-by-step guide:

Translating key words and phrases into algebraic expressions:

- ✓ Addition: plus, more than, the sum of, etc.
- ✓ Subtraction: minus, less than, decreased, etc.
- ✓ Multiplication: times, product, multiplied, etc.
- ✓ Division: quotient, divided, ratio, etc.

Examples:

Write an algebraic expression for each phrase.

1) Eight more than a number is 20.
   More than mean plus a number $= x$
   Then: $8 + x = 20$

2) 5 times the sum of 8 and x.
   Sum of 8 and x: $8 + x$. Times means multiplication. Then: $5 \times (8 + x)$

✎ *Write an algebraic expression for each phrase.*

1) 4 multiplied by x. _____

2) Subtract 8 from y. _____

3) 6 divided by x. _____

4) 12 decreased by y. _____

5) Add y to 9. _____

6) The square of 5. _____

7) x raised to the fourth power. _____

8) The sum of nine and a number. _____

9) The difference between sixty–four and y. _____

10) The quotient of twelve and a number. _____

11) The quotient of the square of x and 7. _____

12) The difference between x and 8 is 22. _____

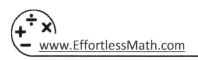

Answers – Day 14

Simplifying Variable Expressions

1) $3x + 27$
2) $-48x + 24$
3) $4x + 3$
4) $-7x^2 - 2$
5) $10x^2 + 5$
6) $15x^2 + 6x$

7) $-7x^2 + 8x$
8) $2x^2 - 3x$
9) $-26x + 12$
10) $90x - 48$
11) $-18x - 59$
12) $2x^2 - 8x$

Simplifying Polynomial Expressions

1) $2x^3 + 3x^2 - 12x$
2) $2x^5 - 5x^3 - 6x^2$
3) $18x^4 + 2x^2$
4) $-12x^3 - 15x^2 + 14x$

5) $-10x^3 + 10x^2 - 3$
6) $4x^4 - 4x^3 - 2x$
7) $-15x^3 - 12x^2 + 8x$
8) $-2x^3 - 3x^2 - 2x$

Translate Phrases into an Algebraic Statement

1) $4x$
2) $y - 8$
3) $\frac{6}{x}$
4) $12 - y$
5) $y + 9$
6) 5^2
7) x^4

8) $9 + x$
9) $64 - y$
10) $\frac{12}{x}$
11) $\frac{x^2}{7}$
12) $x - 8 = 22$

Day 15: Evaluating Variables

Math Topics that you'll learn today:

- ✓ The Distributive Property

- ✓ Evaluating One Variable

- ✓ Evaluating Two Variables

- ✓ Combining like Terms

Mathematics is on the artistic side a creation of new rhythms, orders, designs, harmonies, and on the knowledge side, is a systematic study of various rhythms, orders. - William L. Schaaf

The Distributive Property

Step-by-step guide:

✓ Distributive Property:

$$a(b + c) = ab + ac$$

Examples:

1) Simply. $(5x - 3)(-5) =$

Use Distributive Property formula: $a(b + c) = ab + ac$
$(5x - 3)(-5) = -25x + 15$

2) Simply. $(-8)(2x - 8) =$

Use Distributive Property formula: $a(b + c) = ab + ac$
$(-8)(2x - 8) = -16x + 64$

✎ *Use the distributive property to simply each expression.*

1) $2(2 + 3x) =$

2) $3(5 + 5x) =$

3) $4(3x - 8) =$

4) $(6x - 2)(-2) =$

5) $(-3)(x + 2) =$

6) $(2 + 2x)5 =$

7) $(-4)(4 - 2x) =$

8) $-(-2 - 5x) =$

9) $(-6x + 2)(-1) =$

10) $(-5)(x - 2) =$

11) $-(7 - 3x) =$

12) $8(8 + 2x) =$

Evaluating One Variable

Step-by-step guide:

✓ To evaluate one variable expression, find the variable and substitute a number for that variable.
✓ Perform the arithmetic operations.

Examples:

1) Solve this expression. $12 - 2x$, $x = -1$

First substitute -1 for x, then:

$12 - 2x = 12 - 2(-1) = 12 + 2 = 14$

2) Solve this expression. $-8 + 5x$, $x = 3$

First substitute 3 for x, then:

$-8 + 5x = -8 + 5(3) = -8 + 15 = 7$

✍ *Evaluate each expression using the value given.*

1) $5 + x$, $x = 2$

2) $x - 2$, $x = 4$

3) $8x + 1$, $x = 9$

4) $x - 12$, $x = -1$

5) $9 - x$, $x = 3$

6) $x + 2$, $x = 5$

7) $3x + 7$, $x = 6$

8) $x + (-5)$, $x = -2$

9) $3x + 6$, $x = 4$

10) $4x + 6$, $x = -1$

11) $10 + 2x - 6$, $x = 3$

12) $10 - 3x$, $x = 8$

Evaluating Two Variables

Step-by-step guide:

✓ To evaluate an algebraic expression, substitute a number for each variable and perform the arithmetic operations.

Examples:

1) Solve this expression. $-3x + 5y$, $x = 2, y = -1$

First substitute 2 for x, and -1 for y, then:

$-3x + 5y = -3(2) + 5(-1) = -6 - 5 = -11$

2) Solve this expression. $2(a - 2b), a = -1, b = 3$

First substitute -1 for a, and 3 for b, then:

$2(a - 2b) = 2a - 4b = 2(-1) - 4(3) = -2 - 12 = -14$

✍ *Evaluate each expression using the values given.*

1) $2x + 4y$,

   $x = 3, y = 2$

2) $8x + 5y$,

   $x = 1, y = 5$

3) $-2a + 4b$,

   $a = 6, b = 3$

4) $4x + 7 - 2y$,

   $x = 7, y = 6$

5) $5z + 12 - 4k$,

   $z = 5, k = 2$

6) $2(-x - 2y)$,

   $x = 6, y = 9$

7) $18a + 2b$,

   $a = 2, b = 8$

8) $4x \div 3y$,

   $x = 3, y = 2$

9) $2x + 15 + 4y$,

   $x = -2, y = 4$

10) $4a - (15 - b)$,

   $a = 4, b = 6$

11) $5z + 19 + 8k$,

   $z = -5, k = 4$

12) $xy + 12 + 5x$,

   $x = 7, y = 2$

Combining like Terms

Step-by-step guide:

- ✓ Terms are separated by "+" and "-" signs.
- ✓ Like terms are terms with same variables and same powers.
- ✓ Be sure to use the "+" or "-" that is in front of the coefficient.

Examples:

1) Simplify this expression. $(-5)(8x - 6) =$

Use Distributive Property formula: $a(b + c) = a + ac$
$(-5)(8x - 6) = -40x + 30$

2) Simplify this expression. $(-3)(2x - 2) + 6 =$

First use Distributive Property formula: $a(b + c) = ab + ac$
$(-3)(2x - 2) + 6 = -6x + 6 + 6$

And Combining like Terms:

$-6x + 6 + 6 = -6x + 12$

✎ *Simplify each expression.*

1) $2x + x + 2 =$

2) $2(5x - 3) =$

3) $7x - 2x + 8 =$

4) $(-4)(3x - 5) =$

5) $9x - 7x - 5 =$

6) $16x - 5 + 8x =$

7) $5 - (5x + 6) =$

8) $-12x + 7 - 10x =$

9) $7x - 11 - 2x + 2 =$

10) $12x + 4x - 21 =$

11) $5 + 2x - 8 =$

12) $(-2x + 6)^2 =$

Answers – Day 15

The Distributive Property

1) $6x + 4$
2) $15x + 15$
3) $12x - 32$
4) $-12x + 4$
5) $-3x - 6$
6) $10x + 10$

7) $8x - 16$
8) $5x + 2$
9) $6x - 2$
10) $-5x + 10$
11) $3x - 7$
12) $16x + 64$

Evaluating One Variable

1) 7
2) 2
3) 73
4) -13
5) 6
6) 7

7) 25
8) -7
9) 18
10) 2
11) 10
12) -14

Evaluating Two Variables

1) 14
2) 33
3) 0
4) 23
5) 29
6) -48

7) 52
8) 2
9) 27
10) 7
11) 26
12) 61

Combining like Terms

1) $3x + 2$
2) $10x - 6$
3) $5x + 8$
4) $-12x + 20$
5) $2x - 5$
6) $24x - 5$

7) $-5x - 1$
8) $-22x + 7$
9) $5x - 9$
10) $16x - 21$
11) $2x - 3$
12) $4x^2 - 24x + 36$

Day 16: Equations and Inequalities

Math Topics that you'll learn today:

- ✓ One–Step Equations

- ✓ Multi–Step Equations

- ✓ Graphing Single–Variable Inequalities

"Life is a math equation. In order to gain the most, you have to know how to convert negatives into positives."

– Anonymous

One–Step Equations

Step-by-step guide:

✓ The values of two expressions on both sides of an equation are equal. $ax + b = c$
✓ You only need to perform one Math operation in order to solve the one-step equations.
✓ To solve one-step equation, find the inverse (opposite) operation is being performed.
✓ The inverse operations are:
  - Addition and subtraction
  - Multiplication and division

Examples:

1) Solve this equation. $x + 24 = 0$, $x = ?$
   Here, the operation is addition and its inverse operation is subtraction. To solve this equation, subtract 24 from both sides of the equation: $x + 24 - 24 = 0 - 24$
   Then simplify: $x + 24 - 24 = 0 - 24 \rightarrow x = -24$

2) Solve this equation. $3x = 15, x = ?$
   Here, the operation is multiplication (variable x is multiplied by 3) and its inverse operation is division. To solve this equation, divide both sides of equation by 3:
   $$3x = 15 \rightarrow 3x \div 3 = 15 \div 3 \rightarrow x = 5$$

Solve each equation.

1) $16 = -4 + x, x =$ ____

2) $x - 4 = -25, x =$ ___

3) $x + 12 = -9, x =$ ___

4) $14 = 18 - x, x =$ ___

5) $2 + x = -14, x =$ ___

6) $x - 5 = 15, x =$ ___

7) $25 = x - 5, x =$ ___

8) $x - 3 = -12, x =$ ___

9) $x - 12 = 12, x =$ ___

10) $x - 12 = -25, x =$ ___

11) $x - 13 = 32, x =$ ___

12) $-55 = x - 18, x =$ ___

Multi–Step Equations

Step-by-step guide:

- ✓ Combine "like" terms on one side.
- ✓ Bring variables to one side by adding or subtracting.
- ✓ Simplify using the inverse of addition or subtraction.
- ✓ Simplify further by using the inverse of multiplication or division.

Examples:

1) Solve this equation. $-(2 - x) = 5$

First use Distributive Property: $-(2 - x) = -2 + x$

Now solve by adding 2 to both sides of the equation. $-2 + x = 5 \rightarrow -2 + x + 2 = 5 + 2$

Now simplify: $-2 + x + 2 = 5 + 2 \rightarrow x = 7$

2) Solve this equation. $4x + 10 = 25 - x$

First bring variables to one side by adding x to both sides.

$4x + 10 + x = 25 - x + x \rightarrow 5x + 10 = 25$. Now, subtract 10 from both sides:

$5x + 10 - 10 = 25 - 10 \rightarrow 5x = 15$

Now, divide both sides by 5: $5x = 15 \rightarrow 5x \div 5 = \frac{15}{5} \rightarrow x = 3$

✍ *Solve each equation.*

1) $-3(2 + x) = 3$

2) $-2(4 + x) = 4$

3) $20 = -(x - 8)$

4) $2(2 - 2x) = 20$

5) $-12 = -(2x + 8)$

6) $5(2 + x) = 5$

7) $2(x - 14) = 4$

8) $-28 = 2x + 12x$

9) $3x + 15 = -x - 5$

10) $2(3 + 2x) = -18$

11) $12 - 2x = -8 - x$

12) $10 - 3x = 14 + x$

Graphing Single–Variable Inequalities

Step-by-step guide:

- ✓ Inequality is similar to equations and uses symbols for "less than" (<) and "greater than" (>).
- ✓ To solve inequalities, we need to isolate the variable. (like in equations)
- ✓ To graph an inequality, find the value of the inequality on the number line.
- ✓ For less than or greater than draw open circle on the value of the variable.
- ✓ If there is an equal sign too, then use filled circle.
- ✓ Draw a line to the right or to the left for greater or less than.

Examples:

1) Draw a graph for $x > 2$

Since, the variable is greater than 2, then we need to find 2 and draw an open circle above it. Then, draw a line to the right.

Graph this inequality. $x < 5$

✎ *Draw a graph for each inequality.*

1) $x > -1$

2) $x < 3$

3) $x < -5$

4) $x > -2$

5) $x < 0$

Answers – Day 16

One–Step Equations

1) 20
2) −21
3) −21
4) 4
5) −16
6) 20

7) 30
8) −9
9) 24
10) −13
11) 45
12) −37

Multi–Step Equations

1) −3
2) −6
3) −12
4) −4
5) 2
6) −1

7) 16
8) −2
9) −5
10) −6
11) 20
12) −1

Graphing Single–Variable Inequalities

1)

2)

3)

4)

5)

Day 17: Solving Inequalities

Math Topics that you'll learn today:

- ✓ One–Step Inequalities

- ✓ Multi–Step Inequalities

"Go down deep enough into anything and you will find mathematics." – Dean Schlicter

One–Step Inequalities

Step-by-step guide:

- ✓ Similar to equations, first isolate the variable by using inverse operation.
- ✓ For dividing or multiplying both sides by negative numbers, flip the direction of the inequality sign.

Examples:

1) Solve and graph the inequality. $x + 2 \geq 3$.

Subtract 2 from both sides. $x + 2 \geq 3 \rightarrow x + 2 - 2 \geq 3 - 2$, then: $x \geq 1$

2) Solve this inequality. $x - 1 \leq 2$

Add 1 to both sides. $x - 1 \leq 2 \rightarrow x - 1 + 1 \leq 2 + 1$, then: $x \leq 3$

✍ *Solve each inequality and graph it.*

1) $2x \geq 12$

2) $4 + x \leq 5$

3) $x + 3 \leq -3$

4) $4x \geq 16$

5) $9x \leq 18$

Multi–Step Inequalities

Step-by-step guide:

- ✓ Isolate the variable.
- ✓ Simplify using the inverse of addition or subtraction.
- ✓ Simplify further by using the inverse of multiplication or division.

Examples:

1) Solve this inequality. $2x - 2 \leq 6$

First add 2 to both sides: $2x - 2 + 2 \leq 6 + 2 \rightarrow 2x \leq 8$

Now, divide both sides by 2: $2x \leq 8 \rightarrow x \leq 4$

2) Solve this inequality. $2x - 4 \leq 8$

First add 4 to both sides: $2x - 4 + 4 \leq 8 + 4$

Then simplify: $2x - 4 + 4 \leq 8 + 4 \rightarrow 2x \leq 12$

Now divide both sides by 2: $\frac{2x}{2} \leq \frac{12}{2} \rightarrow x \leq 6$

✎ *Solve each inequality.*

1) $2x - 8 \leq 6$

2) $8x - 2 \leq 14$

3) $-5 + 3x \leq 10$

4) $2(x - 3) \leq 6$

5) $7x - 5 \leq 9$

6) $4x - 21 < 19$

7) $2x - 3 < 21$

8) $17 - 3x \geq -13$

9) $9 + 4x < 21$

10) $3 + 2x \geq 19$

11) $6 + 2x < 32$

12) $4x - 1 < 7$

Answers – Day 17

One–Step Inequalities

1)

2)

3)

4)

5)

Multi–Step inequalities

1) $x \leq 7$
2) $x \leq 2$
3) $x \leq 5$
4) $x \leq 6$
5) $x \leq 2$
6) $x < 10$
7) $x < 12$
8) $x \geq 10 \ \ x \leq 10$
9) $x < 3$
10) $x \geq 8$
11) $x < 13$
12) $x < 2$

Day 18: Lines and Slope

Math Topics that you'll learn today:

- ✓ Finding Slope

- ✓ Graphing Lines Using Slope–Intercept Form

- ✓ Graphing Lines Using Standard Form

"Nature is written in mathematical language." – Galileo Galilei

Finding Slope

Step-by-step guide:

- ✓ The slope of a line represents the direction of a line on the coordinate plane.
- ✓ A coordinate plane contains two perpendicular number lines. The horizontal line is x and the vertical line is y. The point at which the two axes intersect is called the origin. An ordered pair (x, y) shows the location of a point.
- ✓ A line on coordinate plane can be drawn by connecting two points.
- ✓ To find the slope of a line, we need two points.
- ✓ The slope of a line with two points A (x_1, y_1) and B (x_2, y_2) can be found by using this formula: $\frac{y_2 - y_1}{x_2 - x_1} = \frac{rise}{run}$

Examples:

1) Find the slope of the line through these two points: $(2, -10)$ *and* $(3, 6)$.

Slope $= \frac{y_2 - y_1}{x_2 - x_1}$. Let (x_1, y_1) be $(2, -10)$ and (x_2, y_2) be $(3, 6)$. Then: slope $= \frac{y_2 - y_1}{x_2 - x_1} = \frac{6-(-10)}{3-2} = \frac{6+10}{1} = \frac{16}{1} = 16$

2) Find the slope of the line containing two points $(8, 3)$ and $(-4, 9)$.

Slope $= \frac{y_2 - y_1}{x_2 - x_1} \rightarrow (x_1, y_1) = (8,3)$ and $(x_2, y_2) = (-4, 9)$. Then: slope $= \frac{y_2 - y_1}{x_2 - x_1} = \frac{9-3}{-4-8} = \frac{6}{-12} = \frac{1}{-2} = -\frac{1}{2}$

✍ *Find the slope of the line through each pair of points.*

1) $(1, 1), (2, 3)$

2) $(-1, 2), (0, 3)$

3) $(3, -1), (2, 3)$

4) $(-2, -1), (0, 5)$

5) $(5, 1), (2, 4)$

6) $(-3, 1), (-2, 4)$

7) $(6, 2), (7, 4)$

8) $(6, -5), (3, 4)$

9) $(12, -9), (11, -8)$

10) $(7, 4), (5, -2)$

11) $(1, 1), (3, 5)$

12) $(7, -12), (5, 10)$

Graphing Lines Using Slope–Intercept Form

Step-by-step guide:

✓ Slope-intercept form of a line: given the slope m and the y-intercept (the intersection of the line and y-axis) b, then the equation of the line is:

$$y = mx + b$$

Example: *Sketch the graph of* $y = 8x - 3$.

To graph this line, we need to find two points. When x is zero the value of y is -3. And when y is zero the value of x is 3/8. $x = 0 \rightarrow y = 8(0) - 3 = -3$, $y = 0 \rightarrow 0 = 8x - 3 \rightarrow x = \frac{3}{8}$

Now, we have two points: $(0,-3)$ and $(\frac{3}{8},0)$. Find the points and graph the line. Remember that the slope of the line is 8.

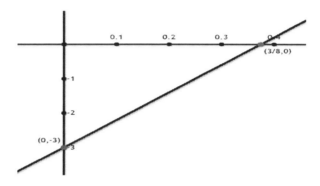

🖎 *Sketch the graph of each line.*

1) $y = \frac{1}{2}x - 4$

2) $y = 2x$

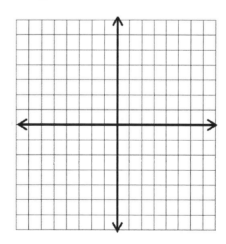

Graphing Lines Using Standard Form

Step-by-step guide:

✓ Find the x –intercept of the line by putting zero for y.

✓ Find the y –intercept of the line by putting zero for the x.

✓ Connect these two points.

Example:

Sketch the graph of $x - y = -5$.

First isolate y for x: $x - y = -5 \rightarrow y = x + 5$

Find the x–intercept of the line by putting zero for y.

$y = x + 5 \rightarrow x + 5 = 0 \rightarrow x = -5$

Find the y–intercept of the line by putting zero for the x.

$y = 0 + 5 \rightarrow y = 5$

Then: x–intercept: $(-5,0)$ and y–intercept: $(0,5)$

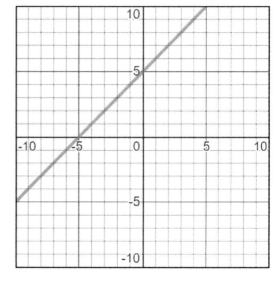

✎ *Sketch the graph of each line.*

1) $y = 3x - 2$ 2) $y = -x + 1$ 3) $x + y = 4$

  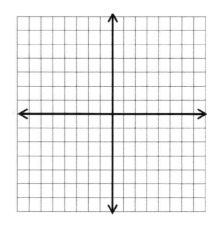

Answers – Day 18

Finding Slope

1) 2
2) 1
3) −4
4) 3
5) −1
6) 3

7) 2
8) −3
9) −1
10) 3
11) 2
12) −11

Graphing Lines Using Slope–Intercept Form

1)

2)

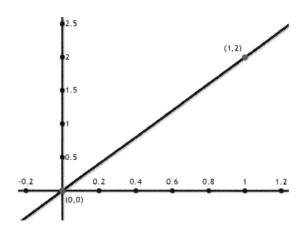

Graphing Lines Using Standard Form

1) $y = 3x - 2$

2) $y = -x + 1$

3) $x + y = 4$

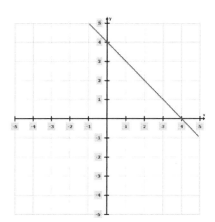

Day 19: Linear Equations and Inequalities

Math Topics that you'll learn today:

- ✓ Writing Linear Equations

- ✓ Graphing Linear Inequalities

- ✓ Finding Midpoint

- ✓ Finding Distance of Two Points

Writing Linear Equations

Step-by-step guide:

- ✓ The equation of a line: $y = mx + b$
- ✓ Identify the slope.
- ✓ Find the y-intercept. This can be done by substituting the slope and the coordinates of a point (x, y) on the line.

Example:

1) What is the equation of the line that passes through $(2, -2)$ and has a slope of 7?

The general slope-intercept form of the equation of a line is $y = mx + b$, where m is the slope and b is the y-intercept.

By substitution of the given point and given slope, we have: $-2 = (2)(7) + b$

So, $b = -2 - 14 = -16$, and the required equation is $y = 2x - 16$.

2) Write the equation of the line through $(2, 1)$ and $(-1, 4)$.

$Slop = \frac{y_2 - y_1}{x_2 - x_1} = \frac{4 - 1}{-1 - 2} = \frac{3}{-3} = -1 \rightarrow m = -1$

To find the value of b, you can use either points. The answer will be the same: $y = -x + b$

$(2, 1) \rightarrow 1 = -2 + b \rightarrow b = 3$

$(-1, 4) \rightarrow 4 = -(-1) + b \rightarrow b = 3$

The equation of the line is: $y = -x + 3$

✍ *Write the equation of the line through the given points.*

1) through: $(1, -2), (2, 3)$

2) through: $(-2, 1), (1, 4)$

3) through: $(-2, 1), (0, 5)$

4) through: $(5, 4), (2, 1)$

5) through: $(-4, 9), (3, 2)$

6) through: $(8, 3), (7, 2)$

7) through: $(7, -2), (5, 2)$

8) through: $(-3, 9), (5, -7)$

Graphing Linear Inequalities

Step-by-step guide:

- ✓ First, graph the "equals" line.
- ✓ Choose a testing point. (it can be any point on both sides of the line.)
- ✓ Put the value of (x, y) of that point in the inequality. If that works, that part of the line is the solution. If the values don't work, then the other part of the line is the solution.

Example:

Sketch the graph of $y < 2x - 3$. First, graph the line:

$y = 2x - 3$. The slope is 2 and y-intercept is -3. Then, choose a testing point. The easiest point to test is the origin: $(0, 0)$

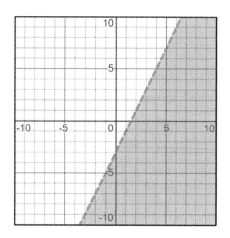

$$(0,0) \rightarrow y < 2x - 3 \rightarrow 0 < 2(0) - 3 \rightarrow 0 < -3$$

0 is not less than -3. So, the other part of the line (on the right side) is the solution.

✎ *Sketch the graph of each linear inequality.*

1) $y > 3x - 1$ 2) $y < -x + 4$ 3) $y \leq -5x + 8$

                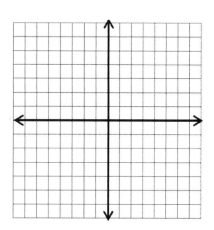

Finding Midpoint

Step-by-step guide:

✓ The middle of a line segment is its midpoint.
✓ The Midpoint of two endpoints A (x_1, y_1) and B (x_2, y_2) can be found using this formula: $M\left(\frac{x_1+x_2}{2}, \frac{y_1+y_2}{2}\right)$

Example:

1) Find the midpoint of the line segment with the given endpoints. $(4, -5), (0, 9)$

Midpoint $= \left(\frac{x_1+x_2}{2}, \frac{y_1+y_2}{2}\right) \to (x_1, y_1) = (4, -5)$ and $(x_2, y_2) = (0, 9)$

Midpoint $= \left(\frac{4+0}{2}, \frac{-5+9}{2}\right) \to \left(\frac{4}{2}, \frac{4}{2}\right) \to M(2, 2)$

2) Find the midpoint of the line segment with the given endpoints. $(6, 7), (4, -5)$

Midpoint $= \left(\frac{x_1+x_2}{2}, \frac{y_1+y_2}{2}\right) \to (x_1, y_1) = (6, 7)$ and $(x_2, y_2) = (4, -5)$

Midpoint $= \left(\frac{6+4}{2}, \frac{7-5}{2}\right) \to \left(\frac{10}{2}, \frac{2}{2}\right) \to (5, 1)$

✎ *Find the midpoint of the line segment with the given endpoints.*

1) $(-2, -2), (0, 2)$

2) $(5, 1), (-2, 4)$

3) $(4, -1), (0, 3)$

4) $(-3, 5), (-1, 3)$

5) $(3, -2), (7, -6)$

6) $(-4, -3), (2, -7)$

7) $(5, 0), (-5, 8)$

8) $(-6, 4), (-2, 0)$

9) $(-3, 4), (9, -6)$

10) $(2, 8), (6, -2)$

11) $(4, 7), (-6, 5)$

12) $(9, 3), (-1, -7)$

Finding Distance of Two Points

Step-by-step guide:

    ✓ Distance of two points A (x_1, y_1) and B (x_2, y_2): $d = \sqrt{(x_1 - x_2)^2 + (y_1 - y_2)^2}$

Example:

1) Find the distance between of $(0, 8), (-4, 5)$.

    Use distance of two points formula: $d = \sqrt{(x_1 - x_2)^2 + (y_1 - y_2)^2}$

    $(x_1, y_1) = (0, 8)$ and $(x_2, y_2) = (-4, 5)$. Then: $d = \sqrt{(x_1 - x_2)^2 + (y_1 - y_2)^2} \rightarrow$

    $d = \sqrt{(0 - (-4))^2 + (8 - 5)^2} = \sqrt{(4)^2 + (3)^2} = \sqrt{16 + 9} = \sqrt{25} = 5 \rightarrow d = 5$

2) Find the distance of two points $(4, 2)$ and $(-5, -10)$.

    Use distance of two points formula: $d = \sqrt{(x_1 - x_2)^2 + (y_1 - y_2)^2}$

    $(x_1, y_1) = (4, 2)$, and $(x_2, y_2) = (-5, -10)$

    Then: $d = \sqrt{(x_1 - x_2)^2 + (y_1 - y_2)^2} \rightarrow d = \sqrt{(4 - (-5))^2 + (2 - (-10))^2} =$

    $\sqrt{(9)^2 + (12)^2} = \sqrt{81 + 144} = \sqrt{225} = 15$. Then: $d = 15$

✎ *Find the distance between each pair of points.*

1) $(2, 1), (-1, -3)$

2) $(-2, -1), (2, 2)$

3) $(-1, 0), (5, 8)$

4) $(-4, -1), (1, 11)$

5) $(3, -2), (-6, -14)$

6) $(-6, 0), (-2, 3)$

7) $(3, 2), (11, 17)$

8) $(-6, -10), (6, -1)$

9) $(5, 9), (-11, -3)$

10) $(9, -3), (3, -11)$

11) $(2, 0), (12, 24)$

12) $(8, 4), (3, -8)$

Answers – Day 19

Writing Linear Equations

1) $y = 5x - 7$
2) $y = x + 3$
3) $y = 2x + 5$
4) $y = x - 1$

5) $y = -x + 5$
6) $y = x - 5$
7) $y = -2x + 12$
8) $y = -2x + 3$

Graphing Linear Inequalities

1) $y > 3x - 1$

2) $y < -x + 4$

3) $y \leq -5x + 8$

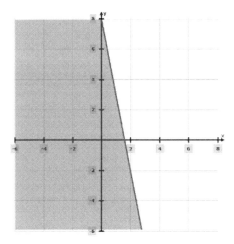

Finding Midpoint

1) $(-1, 0)$
2) $(1.5, 2.5)$
3) $(2, 1)$
4) $(-2, 4)$

5) $(5, -4)$
6) $(-1, -5)$
7) $(0, 4)$
8) $(-4, 2)$

9) $(3, -1)$
10) $(4, 3)$
11) $(-1, 6)$
12) $(4, -2)$

Finding Distance of Two Points

1) 5
2) 5
3) 10
4) 13

5) 15
6) 5
7) 17
8) 15

9) 20
10) 10
11) 26
12) 13

Day 20: Polynomials

Math Topics that you'll learn today:

- ✓ Writing Polynomials in Standard Form

- ✓ Simplifying Polynomials

- ✓ Adding and Subtracting Polynomials

Mathematics is the supreme judge; from its decisions there is no appeal. ~Tobias Dantzig

Writing Polynomials in Standard Form

Step-by-step guide:

✓ A polynomial function $f(x)$ of degree n is of the form
$$f(x) = a_n x^n + a_{n-1} x_{n-1} + \cdots + a_1 x + a_0$$

✓ The first term is the one with the biggest power!

Example:

1) Write this polynomial in standard form. $-12 + 3x^2 - 6x^4 =$

The first term is the one with the biggest power: $-12 + 3x^2 - 6x^4 = -6x^4 + 3x^2 - 12$

2) Write this polynomial in standard form. $5x^2 - 9x^5 + 8x^3 - 11 =$

The first term is the one with the biggest power: $5x^2 - 9x^5 + 8x^3 - 11 =$ $-9x^5 + 8x^3 + 5x^2 - 11$

✎ **Write each polynomial in standard form.**

1) $9x - 7x =$

2) $-3 + 16x - 16x =$

3) $3x^2 - 5x^3 =$

4) $3 + 4x^3 - 3 =$

5) $2x^2 + 1x - 6x^3 =$

6) $-x^2 + 2x^3 =$

7) $2x + 4x^3 - 2x^2 =$

8) $-2x^2 + 4x - 6x^3 =$

9) $2x^2 + 2 - 5x =$

10) $12 - 7x + 9x^4 =$

11) $5x^2 + 13x - 2x^3 =$

12) $10 + 6x^2 - x^3 =$

Simplifying Polynomials

Step-by-step guide:

✓ Find "like" terms. (they have same variables with same power).

✓ Use "FOIL". (First-Out-In-Last) for binomials:

$$(x + a)(x + b) = x^2 + (b + a)x + ab$$

✓ Add or Subtract "like" terms using order of operation.

Example:

1) Simplify this expression. $4x(6x - 3) =$

   Use Distributive Property: $4x(6x - 3) = 24x^2 - 12x$

2) Simplify this expression. $(6x - 2)(2x - 3) =$

   First apply FOIL method: $(a + b)(c + d) = ac + ad + bc + bd$

   $(6x - 2)(2x - 3) = 12x^2 - 18x - 4x + 6$

   Now combine like terms: $12x^2 - 18x - 4x + 6 = 12x^2 - 22x + 6$

✎ *Simplify each expression.*

1) $5(2x - 10) =$

2) $2x(4x - 2) =$

3) $4x(5x - 3) =$

4) $3x(7x + 3) =$

5) $4x(8x - 4) =$

6) $5x(5x + 4) =$

7) $(2x - 3)(x - 4) =$

8) $(x - 5)(3x + 4) =$

9) $(x - 5)(x - 3) =$

10) $(3x + 8)(3x - 8) =$

11) $(3x - 8)(3x - 4) =$

12) $3x^2 + 3x^2 - 2x^3 =$

Adding and Subtracting Polynomials

Step-by-step guide:

✓ Adding polynomials is just a matter of combining like terms, with some order of operations considerations thrown in.
✓ Be careful with the minus signs, and don't confuse addition and multiplication!

Example:

1) Simplify the expressions. $(4x^3 + 3x^4) - (x^4 - 5x^3) =$

First use Distributive Property for $-(x^4 - 5x^3)$, $\rightarrow -(x^4 - 5x^3) = -x^4 + 5x^3$

$(4x^3 + 3x^4) - (x^4 - 5x^3) = 4x^3 + 3x^4 - x^4 + 5x^3$

Now combine like terms: $4x^3 + 3x^4 - x^4 + 5x^3 = 2x^4 + 9$ ³

2) Add expressions. $(2x^3 - 6) + (9x^3 - 4x^2) =$

Remove parentheses: $(2x^3 - 6) + (9x^3 - 4x^2) = 2x^3 - 6 + 9x^3 - 4x^2$

Now combine like terms: $2x^3 - 6 + 9x^3 - 4x^2 = 11x^3 - 4x^2 - 6$

✍ *Add or subtract expressions.*

1) $(-x^2 - 2) + (2x^2 + 1) =$

2) $(2x^2 + 3) - (3 - 4x^2) =$

3) $(2x^3 + 3x^2) - (x^3 + 8) =$

4) $(4x^3 - x^2) + (3x^2 - 5x) =$

5) $(7x^3 + 9x) - (3x^3 + 2) =$

6) $(2x^3 - 2) + (2x^3 + 2) =$

7) $(4x^3 + 5) - (7 - 2x^3) =$

8) $(4x^2 + 2x^3) - (2x^3 + 5) =$

9) $(4x^2 - x) + (3x - 5x^2) =$

10) $(7x + 9) - (3x + 9) =$

11) $(4x^4 - 2x) - (6x - 2x^4) =$

12) $(12x - 4x^3) - (8x^3 + 6x) =$

Answers – Day 20

Writing Polynomials in Standard Form

1) $2x$
2) -3
3) $-5x^3 + 3x^2$
4) $4x^3$
5) $-6x^3 + 2x^2 + x$
6) $2x^3 - x^2$

7) $4x^3 - 2x^2 + 2x$
8) $-6x^3 - 2x^2 + 4x$
9) $2x^2 - 5x + 2$
10) $9x^4 - 7x + 12$
11) $-2x^3 + 5x^2 + 13x$
12) $-x^3 + 6x^2 + 10$

Simplifying Polynomials

1) $10x - 50$
2) $8x^2 - 4x$
3) $20x^2 - 12x$
4) $21x^2 + 9x$
5) $32x^2 - 16x$
6) $25x^2 + 20x$

7) $2x^2 - 11x + 12$
8) $3x^2 - 11x - 20$
9) $x^2 - 8x + 15$
10) $9x^2 - 64$
11) $9x^2 - 36x + 32$
12) $-2x^3 + 6x^2$

Adding and Subtracting Polynomials

1) $x^2 - 1$
2) $6x^2$
3) $x^3 + 3x^2 - 8$
4) $4x^3 + 2x^2 - 5x$
5) $4x^3 + 9x - 2$
6) $4x^3$

7) $6x^3 - 2$
8) $4x^2 - 5$
9) $-x^2 + 2x$
10) $4x$
11) $6x^4 - 8x$
12) $-12x^3 + 6x$

Day 21: Monomials Operations

Math Topics that you'll learn today:

- ✓ Multiplying Monomials

- ✓ Multiplying and Dividing Monomials

- ✓ Multiplying a Polynomial and a Monomial

Mathematics is, I believe, the chief source of the belief in eternal and exact truth, as well as a sensible intelligible world. –
Bertrand Russell

Multiplying Monomials

Step-by-step guide:

  ✓ A monomial is a polynomial with just one term, like $2x$ or $7y$.

Example:

1) Multiply expressions. $5a^4b^3 \times 2a^3b^2 =$

   Use this formula: $x^a \times x^b = x^{a+b}$

   $a^4 \times a^3 = a^{4+3} = a^7$ and $b^3 \times b^2 = b^{3+2} = b^5$

   Then: $5a^4b^3 \times 2a^3b^2 = 10a^7b^5$

2) Multiply expressions. $-4xy^4z^2 \times 3x^2y^5z^3 =$

   Use this formula: $x^a \times x^b = x^{a+b}$

   $x \times x^2 = x^{1+2} = x^3$, $y^4 \times y^5 = y^{4+5} = y^9$ and $z^2 \times z^3 = z^{2+3} = z^5$

   Then: $-4xy^4z^2 \times 3x^2y^5z^3 = -12x^3y^9z^5$

✎ *Simplify each expression.*

1) $4u^9 \times (-2u^3) =$

2) $(-2p^7) \times (-3p^2) =$

3) $3xy^2z^3 \times 2z^2 =$

4) $5u^5t \times 3ut^2 =$

5) $(-9a^6) \times (-5a^2b^4) =$

6) $-2a^3b^2 \times 4a^2b =$

7) $2xy^2 \times x^2y^3 =$

8) $3p^2q^4 \times (-2pq^3) =$

9) $4s^5t^2 \times 4st^3 =$

10) $(-6x^3y^2) \times 3x^2y =$

11) $2xy^2z \times 4z^2 =$

12) $4xy \times x^2y =$

Multiplying and Dividing Monomials

Step-by-step guide:

- ✓ When you divide two monomials you need to divide their coefficients and then divide their variables.
- ✓ In case of exponents with the same base, you need to subtract their powers.
- ✓ Exponent's rules:

$$x^a \times x^b = x^{a+b}, \qquad \frac{x^a}{x^b} = x^{a-b}$$
$$\frac{1}{x^b} = x^{-b}, \quad (x^a)^b = x^{a \times b}$$
$$(xy)^a = x^a \times y^a$$

Example:

1) Multiply expressions. $(-3x^7)(4x^3) =$
   Use this formula: $x^a \times x^b = x^{a+b} \rightarrow x^7 \times x^3 = x^{10}$
   Then: $(-3x^7)(4x^3) = -12x^{10}$

2) Dividing expressions. $\frac{18x^2y^5}{2xy^4} =$
   Use this formula: $\frac{x^a}{x^b} = x^{a-b}$, $\frac{x^2}{x} = x^{2-1} = x$ and $\frac{y^5}{y^4} = y^{5-4} = y$
   Then: $\frac{18x^2y^5}{2xy^4} = 9xy$

✍ *Simplify each expression.*

1) $(-2x^3y^4)(3x^3y^2) =$

2) $(-5x^3y^2)(-2x^4y^5) =$

3) $(9x^5y)(-3x^3y^3) =$

4) $(8x^7y^2)(6x^5y^4) =$

5) $(7x^4y^6)(4x^3y^4) =$

6) $(12x^2y^9)(7x^9y^{12}) =$

7) $\frac{12x^6y^8}{4x^4y^2} =$

8) $\frac{26x^9y^5}{2x^3y^4} =$

9) $\frac{80x^{12}y^9}{10x^6y^7} =$

10) $\frac{95x^{18}y^7}{5x^9y^2} =$

11) $\frac{200x^3y^8}{40x^3y^7} =$

12) $\frac{-15x^{17}y^{13}}{3x^6y^9} =$

Multiplying a Polynomial and a Monomial

Step-by-step guide:

✓ When multiplying monomials, use the product rule for exponents.

✓ When multiplying a monomial by a polynomial, use the distributive property.

$$a \times (b + c) = a \times b + a \times c$$

Example:

1) Multiply expressions. $-4x(5x + 9) =$

Use Distributive Property: $-4x(5x + 9) = -20x^2 - 36x$

2) Multiply expressions. $2x(6x^2 - 3y^2) =$

Use Distributive Property: $2x(6x^2 - 3y^2) = 12x^3 - 6xy^2$

✎ *Find each product.*

1) $3x(9x + 2y) =$

2) $6x(x + 2y) =$

3) $9x(2x + 4y) =$

4) $12x(3x + 9) =$

5) $11x(2x - 11y) =$

6) $2x(6x - 6y) =$

7) $2x(3x - 6y + 3) =$

8) $5x(3x^2 + 2y^2) =$

9) $13x(4x + 8y) =$

10) $5(2x^2 - 9y^2) =$

11) $3x(-2x^2y + 3y) =$

12) $-2(2x^2 - 2xy + 2) =$

Answers – Day 21

Multiplying Monomials

1) $-8u^{12}$
2) $6p^9$
3) $6xy^2z^5$
4) $15u^6t^3$
5) $45a^8b^4$
6) $-8a^5b^3$

7) $2x^3y^5$
8) $-6p^3q^7$
9) $16s^6t^5$
10) $-18x^5y^3$
11) $8xy^2z^3$
12) $4x^3y^2$

Multiplying and Dividing Monomials

1) $-6x^6y^6$
2) $10x^7y^7$
3) $-27x^8y^4$
4) $48x^{12}y^6$
5) $28x^7y^{10}$
6) $84x^{11}y^{21}$

7) $3x^2y^6$
8) $13x^6y$
9) $8x^6y^2$
10) $19x^9y^5$
11) $5y$
12) $-5x^{11}y^4$

Multiplying a Polynomial and a Monomial

1) $27x^2 + 6xy$
2) $6x^2 + 12xy$
3) $18x^2 + 36xy$
4) $36x^2 + 108x$
5) $22x^2 - 121xy$
6) $12x^2 - 12xy$

7) $6x^2 - 12xy + 6x$
8) $15x^3 + 10xy^2$
9) $52x^2 + 104xy$
10) $10x^2 - 45y^2$
11) $-6x^3y + 9xy$
12) $-4x^2 + 4xy - 4$

Day 22: Polynomials Operations

Math Topics that you'll learn today:

- ✓ Multiplying Binomials
- ✓ Factoring Trinomials
- ✓ Operations with Polynomials

Mathematics compares the most diverse phenomena and discovers the secret analogies that unite them. – *Joseph Fourier*

Multiplying Binomials

Step-by-step guide:

✓ Use "FOIL". (First-Out-In-Last)
$$(x + a)(x + b) = x^2 + (b + a)x + ab$$

Example:

1) Multiply Binomials. $(x - 2)(x + 2) =$

Use "FOIL". (First–Out–In–Last): $(x - 2)(x + 2) = x^2 + 2x - 2x - 4$

Then simplify: $x^2 + 2x - 2x - 4 = {}^2 - 4$

2) Multiply Binomials. $(x + 5)(x - 2) =$

Use "FOIL". (First–Out–In–Last):

$(x + 5)(x - 2) = x^2 - 2x + 5x - 10$

Then simplify: $x^2 - 2x + 5x - 10 = x^2 + 3x - 10$

Find each product.

1) $(x + 2)(x + 2) =$

2) $(x - 3)(x + 2) =$

3) $(x - 2)(x - 4) =$

4) $(x + 3)(x + 2) =$

5) $(x - 4)(x - 5) =$

6) $(x + 5)(x + 2) =$

7) $(x - 6)(x + 3) =$

8) $(x - 8)(x - 4) =$

9) $(x + 2)(x + 8) =$

10) $(x - 2)(x + 4) =$

11) $(x + 4)(x + 4) =$

12) $(x + 5)(x + 5) =$

Factoring Trinomials

Step-by-step guide:

- ✓ "FOIL":
$$(x + a)(x + b) = x^2 + (b + a)x + ab$$
- ✓ "Difference of Squares":
$$a^2 - b^2 = (a + b)(a - b)$$
$$a^2 + 2ab + b^2 = (a + b)(a + b)$$
$$a^2 - 2ab + b^2 = (a - b)(a - b)$$
- ✓ "Reverse FOIL":
$$x^2 + (b + a)x + ab = (x + a)(x + b)$$

Example:

1) Factor this trinomial. $x^2 - 2x - 8 =$
Break the expression into groups: $(x^2 + 2x) + (-4x - 8)$
Now factor out x from $x^2 + 2x : x(x + 2)$ and factor out -4 from $-4x - 8: -4(x + 2)$
Then: $= x(x + 2) - 4(x + 2)$, now factor out like term: $x + 2$
Then: $(x + 2)(x - 4)$

2) Factor this trinomial. $x^2 - 6x + 8 =$
Break the expression into groups: $(x^2 - 2x) + (-4x + 8)$
Now factor out x from $x^2 - 2x : x(x - 2)$, and factor out -4 from $-4x + 8: -4(x - 2)$
Then: $= x(x - 2) - 4(x - 2)$, now factor out like term: $x - 2$
Then: $(x - 2)(x - 4)$

✎ *Factor each trinomial.*

1) $x^2 + 8x + 15 =$

2) $x^2 - 5x + 6 =$

3) $x^2 + 6x + 8 =$

4) $x^2 - 8x + 16 =$

5) $x^2 - 7x + 12 =$

6) $x^2 + 11x + 18 =$

7) $x^2 + 2x - 24 =$

8) $x^2 + 4x - 12 =$

9) $x^2 - 10x + 9 =$

10) $x^2 + 5x - 14 =$

11) $x^2 - 6x - 27 =$

12) $x^2 - 11x - 42 =$

Operations with Polynomials

Step-by-step guide:

✓ When multiplying a monomial by a polynomial, use the distributive property.

$$a \times (b + c) = a \times b + a \times$$

Example:

1) Multiply. $5(2x - 6) =$

Use the distributive property: $5(2x - 6) = 10x - 30$

2) Multiply. $2x(6x + 2) =$

Use the distributive property: $2x(6 + 2) = 12x^2 + 4x$

✎ *Find each product.*

1) $9(6x + 2) =$

2) $8(3x + 7) =$

3) $5(6x - 1) =$

4) $-3(8x - 3) =$

5) $3x^2(6x - 5) =$

6) $5x^2(7x - 2) =$

7) $6x^3(-3x + 4) =$

8) $-7x^4(2x - 4) =$

9) $8(x^2 + 2x - 3) =$

10) $4(4x^2 - 2x + 1) =$

11) $2(3x^2 + 2x - 2) =$

12) $8x(5x^2 + 3x + 8) =$

Answers – Day 22

Multiplying Binomials

1) $x^2 + 4x + 4$

2) $x^2 - x - 6$

3) $x^2 - 6x + 8$

4) $x^2 + 5x + 6$

5) $x^2 - 9x + 20$

6) $x^2 + 7x + 10$

7) $x^2 - 3x - 18$

8) $x^2 - 12x + 32$

9) $x^2 + 10x + 16$

10) $x^2 + 2x - 8$

11) $x^2 + 8x + 16$

12) $x^2 + 10x + 25$

Factoring Trinomials

1) $(x + 3)(x + 5)$

2) $(x - 2)(x - 3)$

3) $(x + 4)(x + 2)$

4) $(x - 4)(x - 4)$

5) $(x - 3)(x - 4)$

6) $(x + 2)(x + 9)$

7) $(x + 6)(x - 4)$

8) $(x - 2)(x + 6)$

9) $(x - 1)(x - 9)$

10) $(x - 2)(x + 7)$

11) $(x - 9)(x + 3)$

12) $(x + 3)(x - 14)$

Operations with Polynomials

1) $54x + 18$

2) $24x + 56$

3) $30x - 5$

4) $-24x + 9$

5) $18x^3 - 15x^2$

6) $35x^3 - 10x^2$

7) $-18x^4 + 24x^3$

8) $-14x^5 + 28x^4$

9) $8x^2 + 16x - 24$

10) $16x^2 - 8x + 4$

11) $6x^2 + 4x - 4$

12) $40x^3 + 24x^2 + 64x$

Day 23: System of Equations

Math Topics that you'll learn today:

- ✓ Solving Systems of Equations

- ✓ Systems of Equations Word Problems

Mathematics is a hard thing to love. It has the unfortunate habit, like a rude dog, of turning its most unfavorable side towards you when you first make contact with it. ~ David Whiteland

Systems of Equations

Step-by-step guide:

- ✓ A system of equations contains two equations and two variables. For example, consider the system of equations: $x - y = 1, x + y = 5$
- ✓ The easiest way to solve a system of equation is using the elimination method. The elimination method uses the addition property of equality. You can add the same value to each side of an equation.
- ✓ For the first equation above, you can add $x + y$ to the left side and 5 to the right side of the first equation: $x - y + (x + y) = 1 + 5$. Now, if you simplify, you get: $x - y + (x + y) = 1 + 5 \rightarrow 2x = 6 \rightarrow x = 3$. Now, substitute 3 for the x in the first equation: $3 - y = 1$. By solving this equation, $y = 2$

Example:

What is the value of $x + y$ in this system of equations? $\begin{cases} 3x - 4y = -20 \\ -x + 2y = 10 \end{cases}$

Solving Systems of Equations by Elimination: $\dfrac{\begin{array}{c}3x - 4y = -20\\ -x + 2y = 10\end{array}}{}$ ⇒ Multiply the second equation by 3, then add it to the first equation.

$\dfrac{\begin{array}{l}3x - 4y = -20\\ 3(-x + 2y = 10)\end{array}}{} \Rightarrow \dfrac{\begin{array}{l}3x - 4y = -20\\ -3x + 6y = 30\end{array}}{} \Rightarrow 2y = 10 \Rightarrow y = 5$. Now, substitute 5 for y in the first equation and solve for x. $3x - 4(5) = -20 \rightarrow 3x - 20 = -20 \rightarrow x = 0$

Thus, $x + y = 0 + 5 = 5$

✎ *Solve each system of equations.*

1) $-2x + 2y = 4$ $x = $ ____
   $-2x + y = 3$ $y = $ ____

2) $-10x + 2y = -6$ $x = $ ____
   $6x - 16y = 48$ $y = $ ____

3) $y = -8$ $x = $ ____
   $16x - 12y = 32$

4) $2y = -6x + 10$ $x = $ ____
   $10x - 8y = -6$ $y = $ ____

5) $10x - 9y = -13$ $x = $ ____
   $-5x + 3y = 11$ $y = $ ____

6) $-3x - 4y = 5$ $x = $ ____
   $x - 2y = 5$ $y = $ ____

Systems of Equations Word Problems

Step-by-step guide:

✓ Define your variables, write two equations, and use elimination method for solving systems of equations.

Example:

Tickets to a movie cost $8 for adults and $5 for students. A group of friends purchased **20** tickets for $**115.00**. How many adults ticket did they buy? ____

Let x be the number of adult tickets and y be the number of student tickets. There are 20 tickets. Then: $x + y = 20$. The cost of adults' tickets is $8 and for students it is $5, and the total cost is $115. So, $8x + 5y = 20$. Now, we have a system of equations: $\begin{cases} x + y = 20 \\ 8x + 5y = 115 \end{cases}$

Multiply the first equation by -5 and add to the second equation: $-5(x + y = 20) = -5x - 5y = -100$

$8x + 5y + (-5x - 5y) = 115 - 100 \rightarrow 3x = 15 \rightarrow x = 5 \rightarrow 5 + y = 20 \rightarrow y = 15$. There are 5 adult tickets and 15 student tickets.

✎ *Solve each word problem.*

1) Tickets to a movie cost $5 for adults and $3 for students. A group of friends purchased **18** tickets for $**82.00**. How many adults ticket did they buy? ____

2) At a store, Eva bought two shirts and five hats for $**154.00**. Nicole bought three same shirts and four same hats for $**168.00**. What is the price of each shirt? ____

3) A farmhouse shelters **10** animals, some are pigs, and some are ducks. Altogether there are **36** legs. How many pigs are there? ____

4) A class of **195** students went on a field trip. They took **19** vehicles, some cars and some buses. If each car holds **5** students and each bus hold **25** students, how many buses did they take? ____

Answers – Day 23

Systems of Equations

1) $x = -1, y = 1$
2) $x = 0, y = -3$
3) $x = -4$
4) $x = 1, y = 2$
5) $x = -4, y = -3$
6) $x = 1, y = -2$

Systems of Equations Word Problems

1) 14
2) $32
3) 8
4) 5

Day 24: Triangles, Polygons and Circles

Math Topics that you'll learn today:

- ✓ The Pythagorean Theorem

- ✓ Triangles

- ✓ Polygons

- ✓ Circles

Mathematics is like checkers in being suitable for the young, not too difficult, amusing, and without peril to the state. ~ Plato

The Pythagorean Theorem

Step-by-step guide:

✓ In any right triangle: $a^2 + b^2 = c^2$

Example:

1) Find the missing length.

Use Pythagorean Theorem: $a^2 + b^2 = c^2$

Then: $a^2 + b^2 = c^2 \rightarrow 3^2 + 4^2 = c^2 \rightarrow 9 + 16 = c^2$

$c^2 = 25 \rightarrow c = 5$

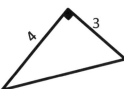

2) Right triangle ABC has two legs of lengths 6 cm (AB) and 8 cm (AC). What is the length of the third side (BC)?

Use Pythagorean Theorem: $a^2 + b^2 = c^2$

Then: $a^2 + b^2 = c^2 \rightarrow 6^2 + 8^2 = c^2 \rightarrow 36 + 64 = c^2$

$c^2 = 100 \rightarrow c = 10$

✍ *Find the missing side.*

1)

2)

3)

4)

5)

6)

7)

8)

Triangles

Step-by-step guide:

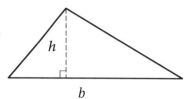

- ✓ In any triangle the sum of all angles is 180 degrees.
- ✓ Area of a triangle = $\frac{1}{2}$ ($base \times height$)

Example:

What is the area of triangles?

1)

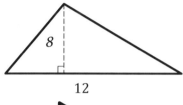

Solution:

Use the are formula: Area $= \frac{1}{2}$ ($base \times height$)

$base = 12$ and $height = 8$

Area $= \frac{1}{2}(12 \times 8) = \frac{1}{2}(96) = 48$

2)

Solution:

Use the are formula: Area $= \frac{1}{2}$ ($base \times height$)

$base = 6$ and $height = 5$

Area $= \frac{1}{2}(5 \times 6) = \frac{30}{2} = 15$

✎ *Find the measure of the unknown angle in each triangle.*

1)

2)

3)

4)

✎ *Find area of each triangle.*

5)

6)

7)

8)

Polygons

Step-by-step guide:

Perimeter of a square $= 4 \times side = 4s$

Perimeter of a rectangle

$= 2(width + length)$

width
length

Perimeter of trapezoid

$= a + b + c + d$

Perimeter of a regular hexagon $= 6a$

Example: Find the perimeter of following regular hexagon.

Perimeter of a parallelogram $= 2(l + w)$

Perimeter of Pentagon $= 6a$

Perimeter of Pentagon $= 6a = 6 \times 3 = 18m$

✍ *Find the perimeter of each shape.*

1)

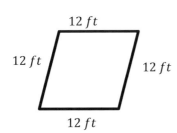

12 ft
12 ft
12 ft
12 ft

2)

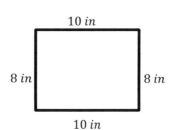

10 in
8 in
8 in
10 in

3)

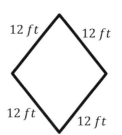

12 ft   12 ft
12 ft   12 ft

4) Square

14 cm

5) Regular hexagon

5 m

6)

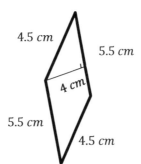

4.5 cm
5.5 cm
4 cm
5.5 cm
4.5 cm

7) Parallelogram

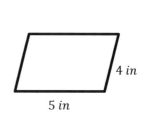

4 in
5 in

8) Square

6 m

Circles

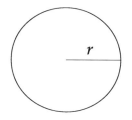

Step-by-step guide:

- ✓ In a circle, variable r is usually used for the radius and d for diameter and π is about 3.14.
- ✓ $Area\ of\ a\ circle = \pi r^2$
- ✓ $Circumference\ of\ a\ circle = 2\pi r$

Example:

1) Find the area of the circle.

Use area formula: $Area = \pi r^2$,

$r = 4$ then: $Area = \pi(4)^2 = 14\pi$, $\pi = 3.14$ then: $Area = 14 \times 3.14 = 43.96$

2) Find the Circumference of the circle.

Use Circumference formula: $Circumference = 2\pi r$

$r = 6$, then: $Circumference = 2\pi(6) = 12\pi$

$\pi = 3.14$ then: $Circumference = 12 \times 3.14 = 37.68$

✎ *Complete the table below.* ($\pi = 3.14$)

	Radius	Diameter	Circumference	Area
Circle 1	4 *inches*	8 *inches*	25.12 *inches*	50.24 *square inches*
Circle 2		12 *meters*		
Circle 3				12.56 *square ft*
Circle 4			18.84 miles	
Circle 5		5 *kilometers*		
Circle 6	6 *centimeters*			
Circle 7		8 *feet*		
Circle 8				28.26 *square meters*

Answers – Day 24

The Pythagorean Theorem

1) 5
2) 17
3) 15
4) 8

5) 5
6) 30
7) 30
8) 12

Triangles

1) 15°
2) 35°
3) 15°
4) 65°

5) 24 *square unites*
6) 30 *square unites*
7) 64 *square unites*
8) 20 *square unites*

Polygons

1) 48 *ft*
2) 36 *in*
3) 48 *ft*
4) 56 *cm*

5) 30 *m*
6) 20 *cm*
7) 18 *in*
8) 24 *m*

Circles

	Radius	Diameter	Circumference	Area
Circle 1	4 *inches*	8 *inches*	25.12 *inches*	50.24 *square inches*
Circle 2	6 *meters*	12 *meters*	37.68 *meters*	113.04 *meters*
Circle 3	2 *square ft*	4 *square ft*	12.56 *square ft*	12.56 *square ft*
Circle 4	3 *miles*	6 *miles*	18.84 *miles*	28.26 *miles*
Circle 5	2.5 *kilometers*	5 *kilometers*	15.7 *kilometers*	19.625 *kilometers*
Circle 6	6 *centimeters*	12 *centimeters*	37.68 *centimeters*	113.04 *centimeters*
Circle 7	4 *feet*	8 *feet*	25.12 *feet*	50.24 *feet*
Circle 8	3 *square meters*	6 *square meters*	18.84 *square meters*	28.26 *square meters*

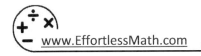

Day 25: Trapezoids, Cubes, Rectangular Prisms and Cylinder

Math Topics that you'll learn today:

- ✓ Trapezoids

- ✓ Cubes

- ✓ Rectangle Prisms

- ✓ Cylinder

Mathematics is as much an aspect of culture as it is a collection of algorithms. – Carl Boyer

Trapezoids

Step-by-step guide:

✓ A quadrilateral with at least one pair of parallel sides is a trapezoid.
✓ Area of a trapezoid $= \frac{1}{2}h(b_1 + b_2)$

Example:

Calculate the area of the trapezoid.

Use area formula: $A = \frac{1}{2}h(b_1 + b_2)$

$b_1 = 12$, $b_2 = 16$ and $h = 18$

Then: $A = \frac{1}{2}18(12 + 16) = 9(28) = 252 \ cm^2$

🖎 *Find the area of each trapezoid.*

1)	2)	3)	4)
			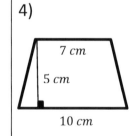

5)	6)	7)	8)

Cubes

Step-by-step guide:

- ✓ A cube is a three-dimensional solid object bounded by six square sides.
- ✓ Volume is the measure of the amount of space inside of a solid figure, like a cube, ball, cylinder or pyramid.
- ✓ Volume of a cube $= (one\ side)^3$
- ✓ surface area of cube $= 6 \times (one\ side)^2$

Example:

Find the volume and surface area of this cube.

2 cm

Use volume formula: $volume = (one\ side)^3$

Then: $volume = (one\ side)^3 = (2)^3 = 8\ cm^3$

Use surface area formula:

$surface\ area\ of\ cube: 6(one\ side)^2 = 6(2)^2 = 6(4) = 24\ cm^2$

✍ *Find the volume of each cube.*

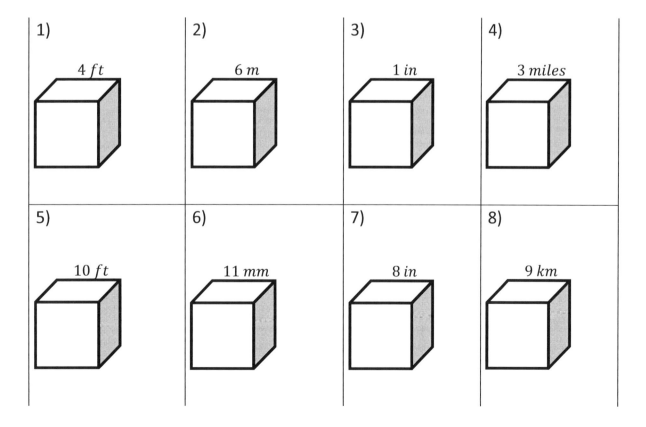

1) 4 ft

2) 6 m

3) 1 in

4) 3 miles

5) 10 ft

6) 11 mm

7) 8 in

8) 9 km

Rectangular Prisms

Step-by-step guide:

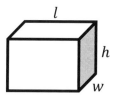

✓ A solid 3-dimensional object which has six rectangular faces.
✓ Volume of a Rectangular prism = **Length × Width × Height**

$Volume = l \times w \times h$ $Surface\ area = 2(wh + lw + lh)$

Example:

Find the volume and surface area of rectangular prism.

Use volume formula: $Volume = l \times w \times h$

Then: $Volume = 10 \times 5 \times 8 = 400\ m^3$

Use surface area formula: $Surface\ area = 2(wh + lw + lh)$

Then: $Surface\ area = 2(5 \times 8 + 10 \times 5 + 10 \times 8) = 2(40 + 50 + 80) = 340\ m^2$

✍ *Find the volume of each Rectangular Prism.*

1)

2)

3)

4)

5)

6)

Cylinder

Step-by-step guide:

✓ A cylinder is a solid geometric figure with straight parallel sides and a circular or oval cross section.
✓ *Volume of Cylinder Formula* $= \pi(radius)^2 \times height$ $\pi = 3.14$
✓ *Surface area of a cylinder* $= 2\pi r^2 + 2\pi rh$

Example:

Find the volume and Surface area of the follow Cylinder.

Use volume formula: $Volume = \pi(radius)^2 \times height$
Then: $Volume = \pi(4)^2 \times 6 = \pi 16 \times 6 = 96\pi$
$\pi = 3.14$ then: $Volume = 96\pi = 301.44$
Use surface area formula: $Surface\ area = 2\pi r^2 + 2\pi rh$
Then: $= 2\pi(4)^2 + 2\pi(4)(6) = 2\pi(16) + 2\pi(24) = 32\pi + 48\pi = 80\pi$
$\pi = 3.14$ then: $Surface\ area = 80 \times 3.14 = 251.2$

✎ *Find the volume of each Cylinder. Round your answer to the nearest tenth.* ($\pi = 3.14$)

1)

2)

3)

4)

5)

6)

Answers – Day 25

Trapezoids

1) $63\ cm^2$
2) $160\ m^2$
3) $24\ ft^2$
4) $42.5\ cm^2$

5) 81
6) 94.5
7) 36
8) 18

Cubes

1) $64\ ft^3$
2) $216\ m^3$
3) $1\ in^3$
4) $27\ miles^3$

5) $1,000\ ft^3$
6) $1,331\ mm^3$
7) $512\ in^3$
8) $729\ km^3$

Rectangle Prisms

1) $210\ m^3$
2) $320\ in^3$
3) $189\ m^3$

4) $150\ cm^3$
5) $576\ ft^3$
6) $240\ m^3$

Cylinder

1) $2,009.6\ m^3$
2) $50.24\ cm^3$
3) $565.2\ cm^3$
4) $2,575.4\ m^3$
5) $904.3\ m^3$
6) $301.4\ in^3$

Day 26: Statistics

Math Topics that you'll learn today:

- ✓ Mean, Median, Mode, and Range of the Given Data

- ✓ Histograms

- ✓ Pie Graph

- ✓ Probability Problems

Millions saw the apple fall, but Newton asked why." - Bernard Baruch

Mean, Median, Mode, and Range of the Given Data

Step-by-step guide:

✓ Mean: $\dfrac{\text{sum of the data}}{\text{total number of data entires}}$

✓ Mode: value in the list that appears most often

✓ Range: the difference of largest value and smallest value in the list

Example:

1) What is the median of these numbers? $4, 9, 13, 8, 15, 18, 5$

Write the numbers in order: $4, 5, 8, 9, 13, 15, 18$

Median is the number in the middle. Therefore, the median is 9.

2) What is the mode of these numbers? $22, 16, 12, 9, 7, 6, 4, 6$

Mode: value in the list that appears most often
Therefore: mode is 6

✍ Solve.

1) In a javelin throw competition, five athletics score $56, 58, 63, 57$ and 61 meters. What are their Mean and Median? _____

2) Eva went to shop and bought 3 apples, 5 peaches, 8 bananas, 1 pineapple and 3 melons. What are the Mean and Median of her purchase? _____

✍ Find Mode and Rage of the Given Data.

3) $8, 2, 5, 9, 1, 2$

Mode: _____   Range: _____

4) $4, 4, 3, 9, 7, 9, 4, 6, 4$

Mode: _____   Range: _____

5) $6, 6, 2, 3, 6, 3, 9, 12$

Mode: _____   Range: _____

6) $12, 9, 2, 9, 3, 2, 9, 5$

Mode: _____   Range: _____

Histograms

Step-by-step guide:

✓ A histogram is an accurate representation of the distribution of numerical data.

Example:

Use the following Graph to complete the table.

Answer:

Day	Distance (km)
1	
2	

→

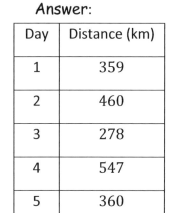

Day	Distance (km)
1	359
2	460
3	278
4	547
5	360

✎ The following table shows the number of births in the US from 2007 to 2012 (in millions).

Year	Number of births (in millions)
2007	4.32
2008	4.25
2009	4.13
2010	4
2011	3.95
2012	3.95

Draw a histogram for the table.

Pie Graph

Step-by-step guide:

- ✓ A Pie Chart is a circle chart divided into sectors, each sector represents the relative size of each value.

Example:

A library has 840 books that include Mathematics, Physics, Chemistry, English and History. Use following graph to answer question.

What is the number of Mathematics books?

Number of total books $= 840$,
Percent of Mathematics books $= 30\% = 0.30$
Then: $0.30 \times 840 = 252$

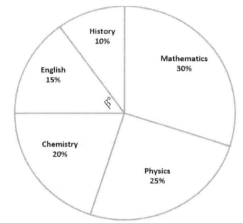

✎ **The circle graph below shows all Jason's expenses for last month. Jason spent $300 on his bills last month.**

1) How much did Jason spend on his car last month? _____

2) How much did Jason spend for foods last month? _____

3) How much did Jason spend on his rent last month? _____

4) What fraction is Jason's expenses for his bills and Car out of his total expenses last month?

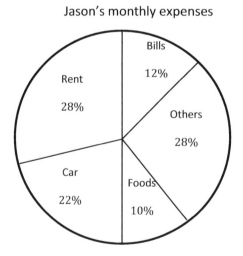

Jason's monthly expenses

Probability Problems

Step-by-step guide:

- ✓ Probability is the likelihood of something happening in the future. It is expressed as a number between zero (can never happen) to 1 (will always happen).
- ✓ Probability can be expressed as a fraction, a decimal, or a percent.

Example:

1) If there are 8 red balls and 12 blue balls in a basket, what is the probability that John will pick out a red ball from the basket?

   There are 8 red ball and 20 are total number of balls. Therefore, probability that John will pick out a red ball from the basket is 8 out of 20 or $\frac{8}{8+12} = \frac{8}{20} = \frac{2}{5}$.

2) A bag contains 18 balls: two green, five black, eight blue, a brown, a red and one white. If 17 balls are removed from the bag at random, what is the probability that a brown ball has been removed?

   If 17 balls are removed from the bag at random, there will be one ball in the bag.

   The probability of choosing a brown ball is 1 out of 18. Therefore, the probability of not choosing a brown ball is 17 out of 18 and the probability of having not a brown ball after removing 17 balls is the same.

✎ *Solve.*

1) A number is chosen at random from 1 to 10. Find the probability of selecting number 4 or smaller numbers. _____

2) Bag A contains 9 red marbles and 3 green marbles. Bag B contains 9 black marbles and 6 orange marbles. What is the probability of selecting a green marble at random from bag A? What is the probability of selecting a black marble at random from Bag B? _____ _____

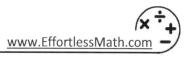

Answers – Day 26

Mean, Median, Mode, and Range of the Given Data

1) Mean: 59, Median: 58

2) Mean: 4, Median: 3

3) Mode: 2, Range: 8

4) Mode: 4, Range: 6

5) Mode: 6, Range: 10

6) Mode: 9, Range: 10

Histograms

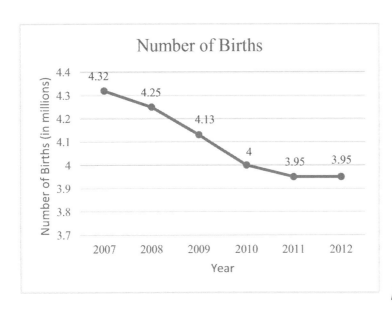

Pie Graph

1) $550
2) $250
3) $700
4) $\frac{17}{50}$

Probability Problems

1) $\frac{2}{5}$

2) $\frac{1}{4}, \frac{3}{5}$

Day 27: Functions

Math Topics that you'll learn today:

- ✓ Function Notation
- ✓ Adding and Subtracting Functions
- ✓ Multiplying and Dividing Functions
- ✓ Composition of Functions

Mathematics is the supreme judge; from its decisions there is no appeal.

-Tobias Dantzig

Function Notation

Step-by-step guide:

- ✓ Functions are mathematical operations that assign unique outputs to given inputs.
- ✓ Function notation is the way a function is written. It is meant to be a precise way of giving information about the function without a rather lengthy written explanation.
- ✓ The most popular function notation is $f(x)$ which is read "f of x".

Example:

1) Evaluate: $w(x) = 3x + 1$, find $w(4)$. Substitute x with 4: Then: $w(x) = 3x + 1 \rightarrow w(4) = 3(4) + 1 \rightarrow w(x) = 12 + 1 \rightarrow w(x) = 13$

2) Evaluate: $h(n) = n^2 - 10$, find $h(-2)$. Substitute x with -2:

   Then: $h(n) = n^2 - 10 \rightarrow h(-2) = (-2)^2 - 10 \rightarrow h(-2) = 4 - 10 \rightarrow h(-2) = -6$

✍ *Evaluate each function.*

1) $f(x) = -x + 5$, find $f(4)$

2) $g(n) = 10n - 3$, find $g(6)$

3) $g(n) = 8n + 4$, find $g(1)$

4) $h(x) = 4x - 22$, find $h(2)$

5) $h(a) = -11a + 5$, find $h(2a)$

6) $k(a) = 7a + 3$, find $k(a - 2)$

7) $h(x) = 3x + 5$, find $h(6x)$

8) $h(n) = n^2 - 10$, find $h(5)$

9) $h(n) = -2n^2 - 6n$, find $h(2)$

10) $g(n) = 3n^2 + 2n$, find $g(2)$

11) $h(x) = x^2 + 1$, find $h(\frac{x}{4})$

12) $h(x) = x^3 + 8$, find $h(-2)$

Adding and Subtracting Functions

Step-by-step guide:

- ✓ Just like we can add and subtract numbers, we can add and subtract functions. For example, if we had functions f and g, we could create two new functions:
- ✓ f + g and f - g.

Example:

1) $f(x) = 2x + 4$, $g(x) = x + 3$, Find: $(f - g)(1)$

$(f - g)(x) = f(x) - g(x)$, then: $(f - g)(x) = 2x + 4 - (x + 3) = 2x + 4 - x - 3 = x + 1$

Substitute x with 1: $(f - g)(1) = 1 + 1 = 2$

2) $g(a) = 2a - 1$, $f(a) = -a - 4$, Find: $(g + f)(-1)$

$(g + f)(a) = g(a) + f(a)$, Then: $(g + f)(a) = 2a - 1 - a - 4 = a - 5$

Substitute a with -1: $(g + f)(a) = a - 5 = -1 - 5 = -6$

✍ *Perform the indicated operation.*

1) $g(x) = 2x - 5$
   $h(x) = 4x + 5$
   Find: $g(3) - h(3)$

2) $h(3) = 3x + 3$
   $g(x) = -4x + 1$
   Find: $(h + g)(10)$

3) $f(x) = 4x - 3$
   $g(x) = x^3 + 2x$
   Find: $(f - g)(4)$

4) $h(n) = 4n + 5$
   $g(n) = 3n + 4$
   Find: $(h - g)(n)$

5) $g(x) = -x^2 - 1 - 2x$
   $f(x) = 5 + x$
   Find: $(g - f)(x)$

6) $g(t) = 2t + 5$
   $f(t) = -t^2 + 5$
   Find: $(g + f)(t)$

Multiplying and Dividing Functions

Step-by-step guide:

- ✓ Just like we can multiply and divide numbers, we can multiply and divide functions. For example, if we had functions f and g, we could create two new functions: f × g, and $\frac{f}{g}$.

Example:

1) $g(x) = -x - 2, f(x) = 2x + 1$, Find: $(g.f)(2)$

$(g.f)(x) = g(x).f(x) = (-x-2)(2x+1) = -2x^2 - x - 4x - 2 = -2x^2 - 5x - 2$

Substitute x with 2:

$(g.f)(x) = -2x^2 - 5x - 2 = -2(2)^2 - 5(2) - 2 = -8 - 10 - 2 = -20$

2) $f(x) = x + 4, h(x) = 5x - 2$, Find: $\left(\frac{f}{h}\right)(-1)$

$\left(\frac{f}{h}\right)(x) = \frac{f(x)}{h(x)} = \frac{x+4}{5x-2}$

Substitute x with -1: $\left(\frac{f}{h}\right)(x) = \frac{x+4}{5x-2} = \frac{(-1)+4}{5(-1)-2} = \frac{3}{-7} = -\frac{3}{7}$

✎ *Perform the indicated operation.*

1) $f(x) = 2a^2$
   $g(x) = -5 + 3a$
   Find $\left(\frac{f}{h}\right)(2)$

2) $g(a) = 3a + 2$
   $f(a) = 2a - 4$
   Find $\left(\frac{g}{f}\right)(3)$

3) $g(t) = t^2 + 3$
   $h(t) = 4t - 3$
   Find $(g.h)(-1)$

4) $g(n) = n^2 + 4 + 2n$
   $h(n) = -3n + 2$
   Find $(g.h)(1)$

5) $f(x) = 2x^3 - 5x^2$
   $g(x) = 2x - 1$
   Find $(f.g)(x)$

6) $f(x) = 3x - 1$
   $g(x) = x^2 - x$
   Find $\left(\frac{f}{g}\right)(x)$

Composition of Functions

Step-by-step guide:

- ✓ The term "composition of functions" (or "composite function") refers to the combining together of two or more functions in a manner where the output from one function becomes the input for the next function.
- ✓ The notation used for composition is: $(f \circ g)(x) = f(g(x))$

Example:

1) Using $f(x) = x + 2$ *and* $g(x) = 4x$, *find:* $f(g(1))$

$(f \circ g)(x) = f(g(x))$

Then: $(f \circ g)(x) = f\big(g(x)\big) = f(4x) = 4x + 2$

Substitute x with 1: $(f \circ g)(1) = 4 + 2 = 6$

2) Using $f(x) = 5x + 4$ *and* $g(x) = x - 3$, *find:* $g(f(3))$

$(f \circ g)(x) = f(g(x))$

Then: $(g \circ f)(x) = g\big(f(x)\big) = g(5x + 4)$, *now substitute x in g(x) by* $5x + 4$. *Then:* $g(5x + 4) = (5x + 4) - 3 = 5x + 4 - 3 = 5x + 1$

Substitute x with 3: $(g \circ f)(x) = g\big(f(x)\big) = 5x + 1 = 5(3) + 1 = 15 = 1 = 16$

✎ *Using* $f(x) = 6x + 2$ *and* $g(x) = x - 5$, *find:*

1) $f(g(7))$

3) $g(f(3))$

2) $f(f(2))$

4) $g(g(x))$

✎ *Using* $f(x) = 7x + 4$ *and* $g(x) = 2x - 4$, *find:*

5) $f(g(3))$

7) $g(f(4))$

6) $f(f(3))$

8) $g(g(5))$

Answers – Day 27

Function Notation

1) 1
2) 57
3) 12
4) -8
5) $-22a + 5$
6) $7a - 11$
7) $18x + 5$

8) 0
9) -20
10) 16
11) $1 + \frac{1}{16}x^2$
12) 15

Adding and Subtracting Functions

1) -16
2) -6
3) -59

4) $n + 1$
5) $-x^2 - 3x - 6$
6) $-t^2 + 2t + 10$

Multiplying and Dividing Functions

1) $-\frac{2}{8} = -\frac{1}{4}$

2) $\frac{11}{2}$

3) -28

4) -7
5) $4x^4 - 12x^3 + 5x^2$
6) $\frac{3x-1}{x^2-x}$

Composition of functions

1) 14
2) 86
3) 15
4) $x - 10$

5) 18
6) 179
7) 60
8) 8

Day 28: Quadratic

Math Topics that you'll learn today:

- ✓ Solve a Quadratic Equation

- ✓ Graphing quadratic functions in vertex form

- ✓ Solving quadratic equations

- ✓ Solve quadratic inequalities

- ✓ Graphing quadratic inequalities

Solving a Quadratic Equation

Step-by-step guide:

- ✓ Write the equation in the form of: $ax^2 + bx + c = 0$
- ✓ Factorize the quadratic and solve for the variable.
- ✓ Use quadratic formula if you couldn't factorize the quadratic.
- ✓ Quadratic formula: $x = \dfrac{-b \pm \sqrt{b^2 - 4ac}}{2a}$

Examples:

Find the solutions of each quadratic.

1) $x^2 + 5x - 6 = 0$

   Use quadratic formula: $= \dfrac{-b \pm \sqrt{b^2 - 4ac}}{2a}$, $a = 1, b = 5$ and $c = -6$

   then: $x = \dfrac{-5 \pm \sqrt{5^2 - 4.1(-6)}}{2(1)}$, $x_1 = \dfrac{-5 + \sqrt{5^2 - 41(-6)}}{2(1)} = 1$, $x_2 = \dfrac{-5 - \sqrt{5^2 - 41(-6)}}{2(1)} = -6$

2) $x^2 + 6x + 8 = 0$

   Use quadratic formula: $= \dfrac{-b \pm \sqrt{b^2 - 4ac}}{2a}$, $a = 1, b = 6$ and $c = 8$

   $x = \dfrac{-6 \pm \sqrt{6^2 - 4.1.8}}{2.1}$, $x_1 = \dfrac{-6 + \sqrt{6^2 - 4.1.8}}{2.1} = -2$, $x_2 = \dfrac{-6 - \sqrt{6^2 - 4.1.8}}{2.1} = -4$

🖎 *Solve each equation.*

1) $x^2 - 2x - 8 = 0$

2) $x^2 - 11x + 19 = -5$

3) $x^2 + 7x + 18 = 8$

4) $x^2 - 10x + 22 = -2$

5) $x^2 + 3x - 12 = 6$

6) $18x^2 + 45x - 27 = 0$

7) $90x^2 - 84x = -18$

8) $x^2 + 8x = -15$

Graphing Quadratic Functions

Step-by-step guide:

- ✓ Quadratic functions in vertex form: $y = a(x - h)^2 + k$ where (h, k) is the vertex of the function. The axis of symmetry is $x = h$
- ✓ Quadratic functions in standard form: $y = ax^2 + bx + c$ where $x = -\frac{b}{2a}$ is the value of x in the vertex of the function.
- ✓ To graph a quadratic function, first find the vertex, then substitute some values for x and solve for y.

Example:

Sketch the graph of $y = 3(x + 1)^2 + 2$.

The vertex of $3(x + 1)^2 + 2$ **is** $(-1, 2)$. Substitute zero for x and solve for y. $y = 3(0 + 1)^2 + 2 = 5$. The y Intercept is $(0, 5)$.

Now, you can simply graph the quadratic function.

📐*Sketch the graph of each function. Identify the vertex and axis of symmetry.*

1) $y = 2(x - 3)^2 + 8$

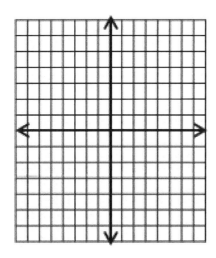

2) $y = x^2 - 8x + 19$

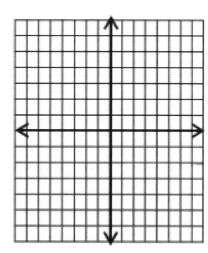

Solving Quadratic Inequalities

Step-by-step guide:

- ✓ A quadratic inequality is one that can be written in one of the following standard forms:

$$ax^2 + bx + c > 0, \ ax^2 + bx + c < 0, \ ax^2 + bx + c \geq 0, \ ax^2 + bx + c \leq 0$$

- ✓ Solving a quadratic inequality is like solving equations. We need to find the solutions.

Examples:

1) **Solve quadratic inequality.** $-x^2 - 5x + 6 > 0$

   Factor: $-x^2 - 5x + 6 > 0 \rightarrow -(x - 1)(x + 6) > 0$

   Multiply both sides by -1: $\left(-(x-1)(x+6)\right)(-1) > 0(-1) \rightarrow (x-1)(x+6) < 0$

   Then the solution could be $-6 < x < 1$ or $-6 > x$ and $x > 1$. Choose a value between -1 and 6 and check. Let's try 0. Then: $-0^2 - 5(0) + 6 > 0 \rightarrow 6 > 0$. This is true! So, the answer is: $-6 < x < 1$

2) **Solve quadratic inequality.** $x^2 - 3x - 10 \geq 0$

   Factor: $x^2 - 3x - 10 \geq 0 \rightarrow (x + 2)(x - 5) \geq 0$. -2 and 5 are the solutions. Now, the solution could be $-2 \leq x \leq 5$ or $-6 \geq x$ and $x \geq 1$. Let's choose zero to check:

   $0^2 - 3(0) - 10 \geq 0 \rightarrow -10 \geq 0$, which is not true. So, $-6 \geq x$ and $x \geq 1$

✎ *Solve each quadratic inequality.*

1) $x^2 + 4x - 5 > 0$

2) $x^2 - 2x - 3 \geq 0$

3) $x^2 - 1 < 0$

4) $17x^2 + 15x - 2 \geq 0$

5) $4x^2 + 20x - 11 < 0$

6) $12x^2 + 10x - 12 > 0$

7) $18x^2 + 23x + 5 \leq 0$

8) $-9x^2 + 29x - 6 \geq 0$

9) $-8x^2 + 6x - 1 \leq 0$

10) $5x^2 - 15x + 10 < 0$

11) $3x^2 - 5x \geq 4x^2 + 6$

12) $x^2 > 5x + 6$

Graphing Quadratic inequalities

Step-by-step guide:

- ✓ A quadratic inequality is in the form $y > ax^2 + bx + c$ (or substitute $<, \le$, or $\ge$ for $>$).
- ✓ To graph a quadratic inequality, start by graphing the quadratic parabola. Then fill in the region either inside or outside of it, depending on the inequality.
- ✓ Choose a testing point and check the solution section.

Example: *Sketch the graph of $y > 2x^2$.*

First, graph $y = 2x^2$

Since, the inequality sing is $>$, we need to use dash lines.

Now, choose a testing point inside the parabola. Let's choose (0,2). $y > 2x^2 \rightarrow 2 > 2(0)^2 \rightarrow 2 > 0$

This is true. So, inside the parabola is the solution section.

✐ *Sketch the graph of each function.*

1) $2y < -4x^2$

2) $y \ge 3x^2$

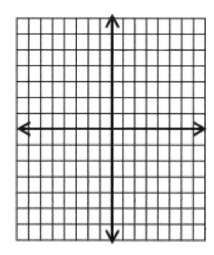

Answers – Day 28

Solving a Quadratic Equation

1) $x = -2, x = 4$

2) $x = 8, x = 3$

3) $x = -5, x = -2$

4) $x = 6, x = 4$

5) $x = -6, x = 3$

6) $x = \frac{1}{2}, x = -3$

7) $x = \frac{3}{5}, x = \frac{1}{3}$

8) $x = -5, x = -3$

Graphing quadratic functions in vertex form

1) $x = 3$ asix of symetry

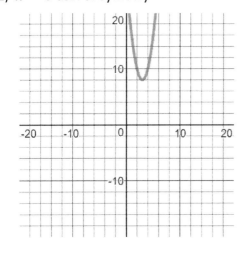

2) $x = 4$ asix of symetry

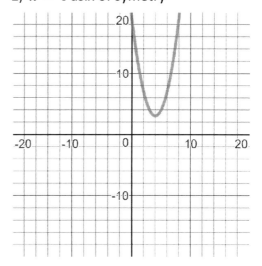

Solve quadratic inequalities

1) $x < -5 \text{ or } x > 1$

2) $x \leq -1 \text{ or } x \geq 3$

3) $-1 < x < 1$

4) $x \leq -1 \text{ or } x \geq \frac{2}{17}$

5) $-\frac{11}{2} < x < \frac{1}{2}$

6) $x < -\frac{3}{2} \text{ or } x > \frac{2}{3}$

7) $-1 \leq x \leq -\frac{5}{18}$

8) $\frac{2}{9} \leq x \leq 3$

9) $x \leq \frac{1}{4} \text{ or } x \geq \frac{1}{2}$

10) $1 < x < 2$

11) $-3 \leq x \leq -2$

12) $x < -1 \text{ or } x > 6$

Graphing quadratic inequalities

1)

2)

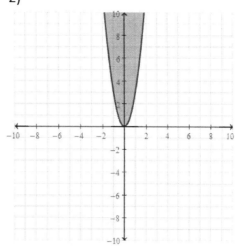

Day 29: Time to Test

Time to refine your skill with a practice examination

Take practice CHSPE Math Tests to simulate the test day experience. After you've finished, score your tests using the answer keys.

Before You Start

- You'll need a pencil, a calculator and scratch papers to take the test.

- For each question, there are four possible answers. Choose which one is best.

- It's okay to guess. There is no penalty for wrong answers.

- Use the answer sheet provided to record your answers.

- After you've finished the test, review the answer key to see where you went wrong.

Good Luck!

CHSPE Math

Practice Test

2020 - 2021

Total number of questions: 50

Total time: No time limit

Basic Calculator is permitted for CHSPE Math Test.

CHSPE Math Practice Test Answer Sheet

Remove (or photocopy) this answer sheet and use it to complete the practice test.

CHSPE Math Practice Test			
1 Ⓐ Ⓑ Ⓒ Ⓓ	16 Ⓐ Ⓑ Ⓒ Ⓓ	31 Ⓐ Ⓑ Ⓒ Ⓓ	46 Ⓐ Ⓑ Ⓒ Ⓓ
2 Ⓐ Ⓑ Ⓒ Ⓓ	17 Ⓐ Ⓑ Ⓒ Ⓓ	32 Ⓐ Ⓑ Ⓒ Ⓓ	47 Ⓐ Ⓑ Ⓒ Ⓓ
3 Ⓐ Ⓑ Ⓒ Ⓓ	18 Ⓐ Ⓑ Ⓒ Ⓓ	33 Ⓐ Ⓑ Ⓒ Ⓓ	48 Ⓐ Ⓑ Ⓒ Ⓓ
4 Ⓐ Ⓑ Ⓒ Ⓓ	19 Ⓐ Ⓑ Ⓒ Ⓓ	34 Ⓐ Ⓑ Ⓒ Ⓓ	39 Ⓐ Ⓑ Ⓒ Ⓓ
5 Ⓐ Ⓑ Ⓒ Ⓓ	20 Ⓐ Ⓑ Ⓒ Ⓓ	35 Ⓐ Ⓑ Ⓒ Ⓓ	50 Ⓐ Ⓑ Ⓒ Ⓓ
6 Ⓐ Ⓑ Ⓒ Ⓓ	21 Ⓐ Ⓑ Ⓒ Ⓓ	36 Ⓐ Ⓑ Ⓒ Ⓓ	
7 Ⓐ Ⓑ Ⓒ Ⓓ	22 Ⓐ Ⓑ Ⓒ Ⓓ	37 Ⓐ Ⓑ Ⓒ Ⓓ	
8 Ⓐ Ⓑ Ⓒ Ⓓ	23 Ⓐ Ⓑ Ⓒ Ⓓ	38 Ⓐ Ⓑ Ⓒ Ⓓ	
9 Ⓐ Ⓑ Ⓒ Ⓓ	24 Ⓐ Ⓑ Ⓒ Ⓓ	39 Ⓐ Ⓑ Ⓒ Ⓓ	
10 Ⓐ Ⓑ Ⓒ Ⓓ	25 Ⓐ Ⓑ Ⓒ Ⓓ	40 Ⓐ Ⓑ Ⓒ Ⓓ	
11 Ⓐ Ⓑ Ⓒ Ⓓ	26 Ⓐ Ⓑ Ⓒ Ⓓ	41 Ⓐ Ⓑ Ⓒ Ⓓ	
12 Ⓐ Ⓑ Ⓒ Ⓓ	27 Ⓐ Ⓑ Ⓒ Ⓓ	42 Ⓐ Ⓑ Ⓒ Ⓓ	
13 Ⓐ Ⓑ Ⓒ Ⓓ	28 Ⓐ Ⓑ Ⓒ Ⓓ	43 Ⓐ Ⓑ Ⓒ Ⓓ	
14 Ⓐ Ⓑ Ⓒ Ⓓ	29 Ⓐ Ⓑ Ⓒ Ⓓ	44 Ⓐ Ⓑ Ⓒ Ⓓ	
15 Ⓐ Ⓑ Ⓒ Ⓓ	30 Ⓐ Ⓑ Ⓒ Ⓓ	45 Ⓐ Ⓑ Ⓒ Ⓓ	

1) In five successive hours, a car traveled $40\ km, 45\ km, 50\ km, 35\ km$ and $55\ km$. In the next five hours, it traveled with an average speed of $65\ km\ per\ hour$. Find the total distance the car traveled in 10 hours.
   A. $425\ km$
   B. $450\ km$
   C. $550\ km$
   D. $600\ km$

2) How long does a $420-$miles trip take moving at 65 miles per hour (mph)?
   A. $4\ hours$
   B. $6\ hours\ and\ 24\ minutes$
   C. $8\ hours\ and\ 24\ minutes$
   D. $8\ hours\ and\ 30\ minutes$

3) Right triangle ABC has two legs of lengths $5\ cm$ (AB) and $12\ cm$ (AC). What is the length of the third side (BC)?
   A. $4\ cm$
   B. $6\ cm$
   C. $8\ cm$
   D. $13\ cm$

4) The ratio of boys to girls in a school is $2\colon 3$. If there are 500 students in a school, how many boys are in the school?
   A. 540
   B. 360
   C. 300
   D. 200

5) $(7x + 2y)(5x + 2y)\ = ?$
   A. $2x^2 + 14xy + 2y^2$
   B. $2x^2 + 4xy + 2y^2$
   C. $7x^2 + 14xy + y^2$
   D. $35x^2 + 24xy\ + 4y^2$

6) Which of the following expressions is equivalent to $5x\ (4 + 2y)$?
   A. $x + 10xy$
   B. $5x + 5xy$
   C. $20xy + 2xy$
   D. $20x + 10xy$

7) If $y = 5ab + 3b^3$, what is y when $a = 2$ and $b = 3$?
   A. 24
   B. 31
   C. 36
   D. 111

8) From the figure, which of the following must be true? (figure not drawn to scale)

   A. $y = z$
   B. $y = 5x$
   C. $y \geq x$
   D. $y + 4x = z$

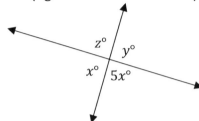

9) The perimeter of the trapezoid below is 64. What is its area?
   A. $252 \ cm^2$
   B. $234 \ cm^2$
   C. $216 \ cm^2$
   D. $260 \ cm^2$

18 cm

12 cm

14 cm

10) Two third of 15 is equal to $\frac{2}{5}$ of what number?
    A. 12
    B. 20
    C. 25
    D. 60

11) The marked price of a computer is D dollar. Its price decreased by 25% in January and later increased by 10% in February. What is the final price of the computer in D dollar?
    A. $0.80 \ D$
    B. $0.82 \ D$
    C. $0.90 \ D$
    D. $1.20 \ D$

12) The radius of a cylinder is 8 inches and its height is 14 inches. What is the surface area of the cylinder?
    A. $64 \ \pi \ in^2$
    B. $128 \ \pi \ in^2$
    C. $192 \ \pi in^2$
    D. $352 \ \pi in^2$

13) The average of 13, 15, 20 and x is 20. What is the value of x?
   A. 9
   B. 15
   C. 18
   D. 32

14) The price of a sofa is decreased by 25% to $450. What was its original price?
   A. $480
   B. $520
   C. $560
   D. $600

15) The area of a circle is 49 π. What is the circumference of the circle?
   A. 7 π
   B. 14 π
   C. 32 π
   D. 64 π

16) A $50 shirt now selling for $28 is discounted by what percent?
   A. 20%
   B. 44%
   C. 54%
   D. 60%

17) In 1999, the average worker's income increased $2,000 per year starting from $26,000 annual salary. Which equation represents income greater than average? (I = income, x = number of years after 1999)
   A. $I > 2000\, x + 26000$
   B. $I > -2000\, x + 26000$
   C. $I < -2000\, x + 26000$
   D. $I < 2000\, x - 26000$

18) A boat sails 60 miles south and then 80 miles east. How far is the boat from its start point?
   A. 45 $miles$
   B. 50 $miles$
   C. 60 $miles$
   D. 100 $miles$

19) Sophia purchased a sofa for $530.40. The sofa is regularly priced at $631. What was the percent discount Sophia received on the sofa?
   A. 12%
   B. 16%
   C. 20%
   D. 25%

20) The score of Emma was half as that of Ava and the score of Mia was twice that of Ava. If the score of Mia was 40, what is the score of Emma?

    A. 10
    B. 15
    C. 20
    D. 30

21) A bag contains 18 balls: two green, five black, eight blue, a brown, a red and one white. If 17 balls are removed from the bag at random, what is the probability that a brown ball has been removed?

    A. $\dfrac{1}{9}$
    B. $\dfrac{1}{6}$
    C. $\dfrac{16}{18}$
    D. $\dfrac{17}{18}$

22) The average of five consecutive numbers is 36. What is the smallest number?

    A. 38
    B. 36
    C. 34
    D. 12

23) The price of a car was $28,000 in 2012. In 2013, the price of that car was $18,200. What was the rate of depreciation of the price of car per year?

    A. 20%
    B. 30%
    C. 35%
    D. 40%

24) The width of a box is one third of its length. The height of the box is one third of its width. If the length of the box is 36 cm, what is the volume of the box?

    A. $81\ cm^3$
    B. $162\ cm^3$
    C. $243\ cm^3$
    D. $1,728\ cm^3$

25) A tree 32 feet tall casts a shadow 12 feet long. Jack is 6 feet tall. How long is Jack's shadow?

    A. $2.25\ feet$
    B. $4\ feet$
    C. $4.25\ feet$
    D. $8\ feet$

26) When a number is subtracted from 28 and the difference is divided by that number, the result is 3. What is the value of the number?
   A. 2
   B. 4
   C. 7
   D. 12

27) An angle is equal to one ninth of its supplement. What is the measure of that angle?
   A. 9
   B. 18
   C. 25
   D. 60

28) John traveled 150 km in 6 hours and Alice traveled 140 km in 4 hours. What is the ratio of the average speed of John to average speed of Alice?
   A. $3:2$
   B. $2:3$
   C. $5:7$
   D. $5:6$

29) If $4n - 3 \geq 1$, what is the least possible value of $4n + 3$?
   A. 3
   B. 4
   C. 7
   D. 9

30) A rope weighs 600 grams per meter of length. What is the weight in kilograms of 14.2 meters of this rope? (1 $kilograms = 1,000\ grams$)
   A. 0.0852
   B. 0.852
   C. 8.52
   D. 8,520

31) A chemical solution contains 6% alcohol. If there is 24 ml of alcohol, what is the volume of the solution?
   A. 240 ml
   B. 400 ml
   C. 600 ml
   D. 1,200 ml

32) The average weight of 18 girls in a class is 56 kg and the average weight of 32 boys in the same class is 62 kg. What is the average weight of all the 50 students in that class?

    A. 50
    B. 59.84
    C. 61.68
    D. 61.90

33) The price of a laptop is decreased by 20% to $360. What is its original price?

    A. $320
    B. $380
    C. $400
    D. $450

34) A bank is offering 4.5% simple interest on a savings account. If you deposit $9,000, how much interest will you earn in five years?

    A. $360
    B. $720
    C. $2,025
    D. $3,600

35) Multiply and write the product in scientific notation:
$$(2.9 \times 10^6) \times (2.6 \times 10^{-5})$$

    A. 754×100
    B. 75.4×10^6
    C. 75.4×10^{-5}
    D. 7.54×10

36) If the height of a right pyramid is 14 cm and its base is a square with side 6 cm. What is its volume?

    A. $432\ cm^3$
    B. $3088\ cm^3$
    C. $236\ cm^3$
    D. $168\ cm^3$

37) 5 less than twice a positive integer is 73. What is the integer?

    A. 39
    B. 41
    C. 42
    D. 44

38) A shirt costing \$300 is discounted 15%. After a month, the shirt is discounted another 15%. Which of the following expressions can be used to find the selling price of the shirt?
   A. $(300)(0.70)$
   B. $(300) - 300(0.30)$
   C. $(300)(0.15) - (300)(0.15)$
   D. $(300)(0.85)(0.85)$

39) Which of the following points lies on the line $2x + 4y = 8$?
   A. $(2, 1)$
   B. $(-1, 3)$
   C. $(-2, 2)$
   D. $(2, 2)$

40) If $2x + 2y = 2$, $3x - y = 7$, which of the following ordered pairs (x, y) satisfies both equations?
   A. $(1, 3)$
   B. $(2, 4)$
   C. $(2, -1)$
   D. $(4, -6)$

41) If $f(x) = 3x + 4(x + 1) + 2$ then $f(4x) = ?$
   A. $28x + 6$
   B. $16x - 6$
   C. $25x + 4$
   D. $12x + 3$

42) A line in the xy-plane passes through origin and has a slope of $\frac{1}{3}$. Which of the following points lies on the line?
   A. $(2,1)$
   B. $(4,1)$
   C. $(9,3)$
   D. $(6,3)$

43) Which of the following is equivalent to $(3n^2 + 2n + 6) - (2n^2 - 4)$?
   A. $n + 4n^2$
   B. $n^2 - 3$
   C. $n^2 + 2n + 10$
   D. $n + 2$

44) Solve for x: $4(x + 1) = 6(x - 4) + 20$
   A. 12
   B. 6.5
   C. 4
   D. 2

$$y < c - x \, , \, y > x + b$$

45) In the xy-plane, if $(0, 0)$ is a solution to the system of inequalities above, which of the following relationships between c and b must be true?

    A. $c < b$
    B. $c > b$
    C. $c = b$
    D. $c = b + c$

46) What is the value of x in the following equation? $3x + 10 = 46$

    A. 4
    B. 7
    C. 10
    D. 12

47) Calculate $f(5)$ for the following function f.

$$f(x) = x^2 - 3x$$

    A. 5

    B. 10

    C. 15

    D. 20

48) John buys a pepper plant that is 5 inches tall. With regular watering the plant grows 3 inches a year. Writing John's plant's height as a function of time, what does the y-intercept represent?

    A. The y-intercept represents the rate of grows of the plant which is 5 inches
    B. The y-intercept represents the starting height of 5 inches
    C. The y-intercept represents the rate of growth of plant which is 3 inches per year
    D. There is no y-intercept

49) If $\frac{4}{x} = \frac{12}{x-8}$ what is the value of $\frac{x}{2}$?

    A. 1
    B. 3
    C. -2
    D. 2

50) If the following equations are true, what is the value of x? $a = \sqrt{3}, \quad 4a = \sqrt{4x}$

    A. 2

    B. 3

    C. 6

    D. 12

End of CHSPE Math Practice Test

CHSPE Mathematics Practice Test Answers and Explanations

Now, it's time to review your results to see where you went wrong and what areas you need to improve!

CHSPE Math Practice Test 1					
1	C	21	D	41	A
2	B	22	C	42	C
3	D	23	C	43	C
4	D	24	D	44	C
5	D	25	A	45	B
6	D	26	C	46	D
7	D	27	B	47	B
8	D	28	C	48	B
9	D	29	C	49	C
10	C	30	C	50	D
11	B	31	B		
12	D	32	B		
13	D	33	D		
14	D	34	C		
15	B	35	D		
16	B	36	D		
17	A	37	A		
18	D	38	D		
19	B	39	A		
20	A	40	C		

CHSPE Mathematics Practice Test Answers and Explanations

1) Choice C is correct

Add the first 5 numbers. $40 + 45 + 50 + 35 + 55 = 225$, To find the distance traveled in the next 5 hours, multiply the average by number of hours. $Distance = Average \times Rate = 65 \times 5 = 325$. Add both numbers. $325 + 225 = 550$

2) Choice B is correct

Use distance formula: $Distance = Rate \times time \Rightarrow 420 = 65 \times T$, divide both sides by $65. 420 \div 65 = T \Rightarrow T = 6.4\ hours.$ Change hours to minutes for the decimal part. $0.4\ hours = 0.4 \times 60 = 24\ minutes.$

3) Choice D is correct

Use Pythagorean Theorem: $a^2 + b^2 = c^2 \Rightarrow 5^2 + 12^2 = c^2 \Rightarrow 169 = c^2 \Rightarrow c = 13$

4) Choice D is correct

Th ratio of boy to girls is $2:3$. Therefore, there are 2 boys out of 5 students. To find the answer, first divide the total number of students by 5, then multiply the result by 2.

$500 \div 5 = 100 \Rightarrow 100 \times 2 = 200$

5) Choice D is correct

Use FOIL (First, Out, In, Last).$(7x + 2y)(5x + 2y) = 35x^2 + 14xy + 10xy + 4y^2 =$

$$35x^2 + 24xy + 4y^2$$

6) Choice D is correct

Use distributive property: $5x(4 + 2y) = 20x + 10xy$

7) Choice D is correct

$y = 5ab + 3b^3$. Plug in the values of a and b in the equation: $a = 2$ and $b = 3$.

$y = 5\,(2)(3) + 3\,(3)^3 = 30 + 3(27) = 30 + 81 = 111$

8) Choice D is correct

x and z are colinear. y and $5x$ are colinear. Therefore,

$x + z = y + 5x, subtract\ x\ from\ both\ sides, then, z = y + 4x$

9) Choice D is correct

The perimeter of the trapezoid is 64. Therefore, the missing side (height) is

$= 64 - 18 - 12 - 14 = 20.$ Area of the trapezoid: $A = \frac{1}{2} h (b_1 + b_2) =$

$$\frac{1}{2} (20) (12 + 14) = 260$$

10) Choice C is correct

Let x be the number. Write the equation and solve for x. $\frac{2}{3} \times 15 = \frac{2}{5} . x \Rightarrow \frac{2 \times 15}{3} = \frac{2x}{5}$, use cross multiplication to solve for x. $5 \times 30 = 2x \times 3 \Rightarrow 150 = 6x \Rightarrow x = 25$

11) Choice B is correct

To find the discount, multiply the number by $(100\% - rate\ of\ discount)$. Therefore, for the first discount we get: $(D)(100\% - 25\%) = (D)(0.75) = 0.75$. For increase of 10%: $(0.75\ D)(100\% + 10\%) = (0.75\ D)(1.10) = 0.82\ D = 82\%\ of\ D$ or $0.82\ D$.

12) Choice D is correct

Surface Area of a cylinder $= 2\pi r\ (r + h)$, The radius of the cylinder is 8 inches and its height is 14 inches. Surface Area of a cylinder $= 2\ (\pi)(8)(8 + 14) = 352\ \pi$

13) Choice D is correct

$\text{average} = \frac{\text{sum of terms}}{\text{number of terms}} \Rightarrow 20 = \frac{13+15+20+x}{4} \Rightarrow 80 = 48 + x \Rightarrow x = 32$

14) Choice D is correct

Let x be the original price. If the price of the sofa is decreased by 25% to \$450, then: $75\%\ of\ x = 450 \Rightarrow 0.75x = 450 \Rightarrow x = 450 \div 0.75 = 600$

15) Choice B is correct

Use the formula of areas of circles. $Area = \pi r^2 \Rightarrow 49\pi = \pi r^2 \Rightarrow 49 = r^2 \Rightarrow r = 7$

Radius of the circle is 7. Now, use the circumference formula: Circumference $=$

$2\pi r = 2\pi\ (7) = 14\ \pi.$

16) Choice B is correct

Use the formula for Percent of Change. $\frac{\text{New Value}-\text{Old Value}}{Old\ Value} \times 100\%$.

$\frac{28-50}{50} \times 100\ \% = -44\%$ (negative sign here means that the new price is less than old price).

17) Choice A is correct

Let x be the number of years. Therefore, \$2,000 per year equals $2000x$. starting from \$26,000 annual salary means you should add that amount to $2000x$. Income more than that is:

$I > 2000\ x + 26000$

www.EffortlessMath.com

18) Choice D is correct

Use the information provided in the question to draw the shape.

60 *miles*

80 *miles*

Use Pythagorean Theorem: $a^2 + b^2 = c^2$

$60^2 + 80^2 = c^2 \Rightarrow 3600 + 6400 = c^2 \Rightarrow 10000 = c^2 \Rightarrow c = 100$

19) Choice B is correct

The question is this: 530.40 is what percent of 631?

$percent = \frac{530.40}{631} = 84.05 \cong 84.$ 530.40 is 84% of 631. Therefore, the discount is:

$100\% - 84\% = 16\%$

20) Choice A is correct

If the score of Mia was 40, therefore the score of Ava is 20. Since, the score of Emma was half as that of Ava, therefore, the score of Emma is 10.

21) Choice D is correct

If 17 balls are removed from the bag at random, there will be one ball in the bag. The probability of choosing a brown ball is 1 out of 18. Therefore, the probability of not choosing a brown ball is 17 out of 18 and the probability of having not a brown ball after removing 17 balls is the same.

22) Choice C is correct

Let x be the smallest number. Then, these are the numbers: $x, x + 1, x + 2, x + 3, x + 4$

$$\text{average} = \frac{\text{sum of terms}}{\text{number of terms}} \Rightarrow 36 = \frac{x+(x+1)+(x+2)+(x+3)+(x+4)}{5} \Rightarrow 36 = \frac{5x+10}{5} \Rightarrow$$

$$180 = 5x + 10 \Rightarrow 170 = 5x \Rightarrow x = 34$$

23) Choice C is correct

Use this formula: Percent of Change: $\frac{\text{New Value} - \text{Old Value}}{\text{Old Value}} \times 100\%$.

$\frac{18,200 - 28,000}{28,000} \times 100\% = -35\%$. The negative sign means that the price decreased.

24) Choice D is correct

If the length of the box is 36, then the width of the box is one third of it, 12, and the height of the box is 4 (one third of the width). The volume of the box is: $V = lwh = (36)(12)(4) = 1,728$

25) Choice A is correct

Write a proportion and solve for the missing number. $\frac{32}{12} = \frac{6}{x} \rightarrow 32x = 6 \times 12 = 72$

$$32x = 72 \rightarrow x = \frac{72}{32} = 2.25$$

26) Choice C is correct

Let x be the number. Write the equation and solve for x. $(28 - x) \div x = 3$

Multiply both sides by x. $(28 - x) = 3x$, then add x both sides. $28 = 4x$, now divide both sides by 4. $x = 7$

27) Choice B is correct

The sum of supplement angles is 180. Let x be that angle. Therefore, $x + 9x = 180$

$10x = 180$, divide both sides by 10: $x = 18$

28) Choice C is correct

The average speed of john is: $150 \div 6 = 25$, The average speed of Alice is: $140 \div 4 = 35$

Write the ratio and simplify. $25 : 35 \Rightarrow 5 : 7$

29) Choice C is correct

Adding 6 to each side of the inequality $4n - 3 \geq 1$ yields the inequality $4n + 3 \geq 7$. Therefore, the least possible value of $4n + 3$ is 7.

30) Choice C is correct

The weight of 14.2 meters of this rope is: $14.2 \times 600 \, g = 8520 \, g$

$1 \, kg = 1000 \, g$, therefore, $8520 \, g \div 1,000 = 8.52 \, kg$

31) Choice B is correct

6% of the volume of the solution is alcohol. Let x be the volume of the solution.

Then: $6\% \; of \; x = 24 \, ml \Rightarrow 0.06 \, x = 24 \Rightarrow x = 24 \div 0.06 = 400$

32) Choice B is correct

$average = \frac{sum \; of \; terms}{number \; of \; terms}$. The sum of the weight of all girls is: $18 \times 56 = 1,008 \, kg$

The sum of the weight of all boys is: $32 \times 62 = 1,984 \, kg$. The sum of the weight of all students is: $1,008 + 1,984 = 2,992 \, kg$. $average = \frac{2992}{50} = 59.84$

33) Choice D is correct

Let x be the original price. If the price of a laptop is decreased by 20% to $360, then: 80% *of*

$x = 360 \Rightarrow 0.80x = 360 \Rightarrow x = 360 \div 0.80 = 450$

34) Choice C is correct

Use simple interest formula: $I = prt$. (I = interest, p = principal, r = rate, t = time). $I = (9,000)(0.045)(5) = 2,025$

35) Choice D is correct

$(2.9 \times 10^6) \times (2.6 \times 10^{-5}) = (2.9 \times 2.6) \times (10^6 \times 10^{-5}) = 7.54 \times (10^{6+(-5)})$
$$= 7.54 \times 10^1$$

36) Choice D is correct

The formula of the volume of pyramid is: $V = \frac{l \times w \times h}{3}$

The length and width of the pyramid is $6\ cm$ and its height is $14\ cm$. Therefore:

$$V = \frac{6 \times 6 \times 14}{3} = 168\ cm^3$$

37) Choice A is correct

Let x be the integer. Then: $2x - 5 = 73$, Add 5 both sides: $2x = 78$, Divide both sides by 2:

$$x = 39$$

38) Choice D is correct

To find the discount, multiply the number by $(100\% - ate\ of\ discount)$. Therefore, for the first discount we get: $(300)(100\% - 15\%) = (300)(0.85)$. For the next 15% discount: $(300)(0.85)(0.85)$.

39) Choice A is correct

Plug in each pair of number in the equation: $2x + 4y = 8$

A. $(2, 1)$: $2(2) + 4(1) = 8$
B. $(-1, 3)$: $2(-1) + 4(3) = 10$
C. $(-2, 2)$: $2(-2) + 4(2) = 4$
D. $(2, 2)$: $2(2) + 4(2) = 12$

Only choice A is correct.

40) Choice C is correct

Plugin the values of x and y provided in the choices into both equations. Let's start with $2x + 2y = 2$:

A. $(1, 3)$ $2x + 2y = 2 \rightarrow 2 + 6 \neq 2$
B. $(2, 4)$ $2x + y = 2 \rightarrow 4 + 8 \neq 2$
C. $(2, -1)$ $2x + 2y = 2 \rightarrow 4 + (-2) = 2$
D. $(4, -6)$ $2x + 2y = 2 \rightarrow 12 + (-12) \neq 2$

Only choice C is correct.

41) Choice A is correct

If $f(x) = 3x + 4(x + 1) + 2$, then find $f(4x)$ by substituting $4x$ for every x in the function. This gives: $f(4x) = 3(4x) + 4(4x + 1) + 2$

It simplifies to: $f(4x) = 3(4x) + 4(4x + 1) + 2 = 12x + 16x + 4 + 2 = 28x + 6$

42) Choice C is correct

First, find the equation of the line. All lines through the origin are of the form $y = mx$, so the equation is $y = \frac{1}{3}x$. Of the given choices, only choice C $(9,3)$, satisfies this equation:

$$y = \frac{1}{3}x \rightarrow 3 = \frac{1}{3}(9) = 3$$

43) Choice C is correct

$(3n^2 + 2n + 6) - (2n^2 - 4)$. Add like terms together: $3n^2 - 2n^2 = n^2$, $2n$ doesn't have like terms. $6 - (-4) = 10$, Combine these terms into one expression to find the answer: $n^2 + 2n + 10$

44) Choice C is correct

Simplify and solve for x in the equation. $4(x + 1) = 6(x - 4) + 20$, $4x + 4 = 6x - 24 + 20$, $4x + 4 = 6x - 4$. Subtract $4x$ from both sides: $4 = 2x - 4$, Add 4 to both sides: $8 = 2x$, $4 = x$

45) Choice B is correct

Since $(0, 0)$ is a solution to the system of inequalities, substituting 0 for x and 0 for y in the given system must result in two true inequalities. After this substitution, $y < c - x$ becomes $0 < a$, and $y > x + b$ becomes $0 > b$. Hence, a is positive and b is negative.
Therefore, $c > b$.

46) Choice D is correct

$$3x + 10 = 46 \rightarrow 3x = 46 - 10 = 36 \rightarrow x = \frac{36}{3} = 12$$

47) Choice B is correct

The input value is 5. Then: $x = 5$. $f(x) = x^2 - 3x \rightarrow f(5) = 5^2 - 3(5) = 25 - 15 = 10$

48) Choice B is correct

To solve this problem, first recall the equation of a line: $y = mx + b$

Where $m = slope.$ $y = y - intercept$

Remember that slope is the rate of change that occurs in a function and that the $y-$intercept is the y value corresponding to $x = 0$.

Since the height of John's plant is 5 inches tall when he gets it. Time (or x) is zero. The plant grows 3 inches per year. Therefore, the rate of change of the plant's height is 3. The $y-$intercept represents the starting height of the plant which is 5 inches.

49) Choice C is correct

Multiplying each side of $\frac{4}{x} = \frac{12}{x-8}$ by $x(x-8)$ gives $4(x-8) = 12(x)$, distributing the 4 over the values within the parentheses yields $x - 8 = 3x$ or $x = -4$.

Therefore, the value of $\frac{x}{2} = \frac{-4}{2} = -2$.

50) Choice D is correct

Given the two equations, substitute the numerical value of a into the second equation to solve for x. $a = \sqrt{3}$, $4a = \sqrt{4x}$

Substituting the numerical value for a into the equation with x is as follows.

$4(\sqrt{3}) = \sqrt{4x}$,   From here, distribute the 4. $4\sqrt{3} = \sqrt{4x}$

Now square both side of the equation. $(4\sqrt{3})^2 = (\sqrt{4x})^2$

Remember to square both terms within the parentheses. Also, recall that squaring a square root sign cancels them out. $4^2\sqrt{3}^2 = 4x$, $16(3) = 4x$, $48 = 4x$, $x = 12$

Day 30: A Realistic CHSPE Math Test

Time to refine your skill with a practice examination

Take practice CHSPE Math Tests to simulate the test day experience. After you've finished, score your tests using the answer keys.

Before You Start

- You'll need a pencil, a calculator and scratch papers to take the test.

- For each question, there are four possible answers. Choose which one is best.

- It's okay to guess. There is no penalty for wrong answers.

- Use the answer sheet provided to record your answers.

- After you've finished the test, review the answer key to see where you went wrong.

Good Luck!

CHSPE Math

Practice Test

2020 - 2021

Total number of questions: 50

Total time: No time limit

Basic Calculator is permitted for CHSPE Math Test.

CHSPE Math Practice Test Answer Sheet

Remove (or photocopy) this answer sheet and use it to complete the practice test.

CHSPE Math Practice Test			
1 Ⓐ Ⓑ Ⓒ Ⓓ	16 Ⓐ Ⓑ Ⓒ Ⓓ	31 Ⓐ Ⓑ Ⓒ Ⓓ	46 Ⓐ Ⓑ Ⓒ Ⓓ
2 Ⓐ Ⓑ Ⓒ Ⓓ	17 Ⓐ Ⓑ Ⓒ Ⓓ	32 Ⓐ Ⓑ Ⓒ Ⓓ	47 Ⓐ Ⓑ Ⓒ Ⓓ
3 Ⓐ Ⓑ Ⓒ Ⓓ	18 Ⓐ Ⓑ Ⓒ Ⓓ	33 Ⓐ Ⓑ Ⓒ Ⓓ	48 Ⓐ Ⓑ Ⓒ Ⓓ
4 Ⓐ Ⓑ Ⓒ Ⓓ	19 Ⓐ Ⓑ Ⓒ Ⓓ	34 Ⓐ Ⓑ Ⓒ Ⓓ	39 Ⓐ Ⓑ Ⓒ Ⓓ
5 Ⓐ Ⓑ Ⓒ Ⓓ	20 Ⓐ Ⓑ Ⓒ Ⓓ	35 Ⓐ Ⓑ Ⓒ Ⓓ	50 Ⓐ Ⓑ Ⓒ Ⓓ
6 Ⓐ Ⓑ Ⓒ Ⓓ	21 Ⓐ Ⓑ Ⓒ Ⓓ	36 Ⓐ Ⓑ Ⓒ Ⓓ	
7 Ⓐ Ⓑ Ⓒ Ⓓ	22 Ⓐ Ⓑ Ⓒ Ⓓ	37 Ⓐ Ⓑ Ⓒ Ⓓ	
8 Ⓐ Ⓑ Ⓒ Ⓓ	23 Ⓐ Ⓑ Ⓒ Ⓓ	38 Ⓐ Ⓑ Ⓒ Ⓓ	
9 Ⓐ Ⓑ Ⓒ Ⓓ	24 Ⓐ Ⓑ Ⓒ Ⓓ	39 Ⓐ Ⓑ Ⓒ Ⓓ	
10 Ⓐ Ⓑ Ⓒ Ⓓ	25 Ⓐ Ⓑ Ⓒ Ⓓ	40 Ⓐ Ⓑ Ⓒ Ⓓ	
11 Ⓐ Ⓑ Ⓒ Ⓓ	26 Ⓐ Ⓑ Ⓒ Ⓓ	41 Ⓐ Ⓑ Ⓒ Ⓓ	
12 Ⓐ Ⓑ Ⓒ Ⓓ	27 Ⓐ Ⓑ Ⓒ Ⓓ	42 Ⓐ Ⓑ Ⓒ Ⓓ	
13 Ⓐ Ⓑ Ⓒ Ⓓ	28 Ⓐ Ⓑ Ⓒ Ⓓ	43 Ⓐ Ⓑ Ⓒ Ⓓ	
14 Ⓐ Ⓑ Ⓒ Ⓓ	29 Ⓐ Ⓑ Ⓒ Ⓓ	44 Ⓐ Ⓑ Ⓒ Ⓓ	
15 Ⓐ Ⓑ Ⓒ Ⓓ	30 Ⓐ Ⓑ Ⓒ Ⓓ	45 Ⓐ Ⓑ Ⓒ Ⓓ	

1) The mean of 50 test scores was calculated as 90. But, it turned out that one of the scores was misread as 94 but it was 69. What is the mean?
   A. 85
   B. 87
   C. 89.5
   D. 90.5

2) Two dice are thrown simultaneously, what is the probability of getting a sum of 5 or 8?
   A. $\dfrac{1}{3}$
   B. $\dfrac{11}{36}$
   C. $\dfrac{1}{16}$
   D. $\dfrac{1}{4}$

3) Which of the following is equal to the expression below?

$$(5x + 2y)(2x - y)$$

   A. $4x^2 - 2y^2$
   B. $2x^2 + 6xy - 2y^2$
   C. $24x^2 + 2xy - 2y^2$
   D. $10x^2 - xy - 2y^2$

4) What is the product of all possible values of x in the following equation?

$$|x - 10| = 4$$

   A. 3
   B. 7
   C. 13
   D. 84

5) What is the slope of a line that is perpendicular to the line $4x - 2y = 6$?
   A. -2
   B. $-\dfrac{1}{2}$
   C. 4
   D. 12

6) What is the value of the expression $6(x - 2y) + (2 - x)^2$ when $x = 3$ and $y = -2$?
   A. -4
   B. 20
   C. 43
   D. 50

7) A swimming pool holds 2,500 cubic feet of water. The swimming pool is 25 feet long and 10 feet wide. How deep is the swimming pool?
   A. $2\ feet$
   B. $4\ feet$
   C. $6\ feet$
   D. $10\ feet$

8) Four one – foot rulers can be split among how many users to leave each with $\frac{1}{3}$ of a ruler?
   A. 4
   B. 6
   C. 12
   D. 24

9) What is the area of a square whose diagonal is 4?
   A. 4
   B. 8
   C. 16
   D. 64

10) The average of five numbers is 26. If a sixth number 42 is added, then, what is the new average? (round your answer to the nearest hundredth)
   A. 25
   B. 26.5
   C. 27
   D. 28.66

Questions 11 to 13 are based on the following data

The result of a research shows the number of men and women in four cities of a country.

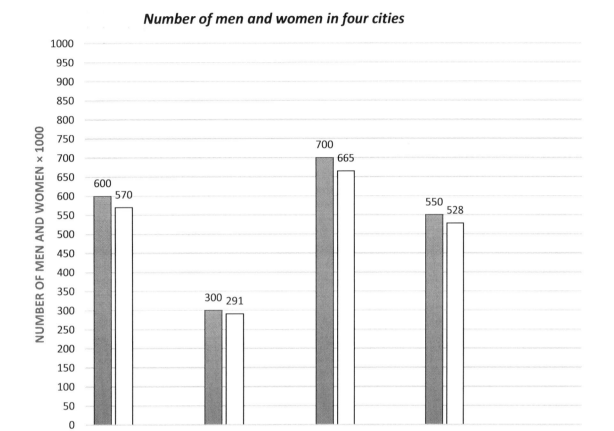

Number of men and women in four cities

11) What's the maximum ratio of the number of women to number of men in each city?

A. 0.98

B. 0.97

C. 0.96

D. 0.95

12) What's the ratio of the percentage of men in city A to percentage of women in city C?

    A. $\dfrac{10}{9}$

    B. $\dfrac{9}{10}$

    C. 1

    D. $\dfrac{20}{19}$

13) How many women should be added to city D to change the ratio of women to men to 1.2?

    A. 130

    B. 129

    C. 132

    D. 131

14) Jason needs an 70% average in his writing class to pass. On his first 4 exams, he earned scores of 68%, 72%, 85%, and 90%. What is the minimum score Jason can earn on his fifth and final test to pass?

    A. 80%,

    B. 70%

    C. 68%

    D. 35%

15) What is the value of x in the following equation? $\dfrac{2}{3}x + \dfrac{1}{6} = \dfrac{1}{2}$

    A. 6

    B. $\dfrac{1}{2}$

    C. $\dfrac{1}{3}$

    D. $\dfrac{1}{4}$

16) A bank is offering 4.5% simple interest on a savings account. If you deposit $12,000, how much interest will you earn in two years?

    A. $420

    B. $1,080

    C. $4,200

    D. $8,400

17) Simplify $7x^2y^3(2x^2y)^3 =$

    A. $12x^4y^6$

    B. $12x^8y^6$

    C. $56x^4y^6$

    D. $56x^8y^6$

18) What is the surface area of the cylinder below?

4 in

8 in

   A. $40 \pi\ in^2$
   B. $57 \pi\ in^2$
   C. $66 \pi\ in^2$
   D. $288 \pi\ in^2$
   E. $400 \pi\ in^2$

19) Last week 25,000 fans attended a football match. This week three times as many bought tickets, but one sixth of them cancelled their tickets. How many are attending this week?
   A. 48,000
   B. 54,000
   C. 62,500
   D. 75,000

20) What is the perimeter of a square that has an area of 49 square inches?
   A. $144\ inches$
   B. $64\ inches$
   C. $56\ inches$
   D. $28\ inches$

21) If $f(x)=2x^3+ 5x^2+ 2x$ and $g(x)= -4$, what is the value of $f(g(x))$?

   A. 56
   B. 32
   C. 24
   D. -56

22) A cruise line ship left Port A and traveled 50 miles due west and then 120 miles due north. At this point, what is the shortest distance from the cruise to port A?
   A. $70\ miles$
   B. $80\ miles$
   C. $150\ miles$
   D. $130\ miles$

23) What is the equivalent temperature of $104°F$ in Celsius?

$$C = \frac{5}{9}\ (F - 32)$$

   A. 32
   B. 40
   C. 48
   D. 52

24) The perimeter of a rectangular yard is 72 meters. What is its length if its width is twice its length?

    A. 12 *meters*

    B. 18 *meters*

    C. 20 *meters*

    D. 24 *meters*

25) The average of 6 numbers is 14. The average of 4 of those numbers is 10. What is the average of the other two numbers?

    A. 10

    B. 12

    C. 14

    D. 22

26) If 150% of a number is 75, then what is the 80% of that number?

    A. 40

    B. 50

    C. 70

    D. 85

27) What is the slope of the line: $4x - 2y = 12$

    A. -1

    B. -2

    C. 1

    D. 2

28) In two successive years, the population of a town is increased by 10% and 20%. What percent of the population is increased after two years?

    A. 30%

    B. 32%

    C. 35%

    D. 68%

29) The area of a circle is 36π. What is the diameter of the circle?

    A. 4

    B. 8

    C. 12

    D. 14

30) If 20% of a number is 4, what is the number?

    A. 4

    B. 8

    C. 10

    D. 20

31) If a tree casts a 26–foot shadow at the same time that a 3 feet yardstick casts a 2–foot shadow, what is the height of the tree?

    A. $24\ ft$
    B. $28\ ft$
    C. $39\ ft$
    D. $48\ ft$

32) Jason is 9 miles ahead of Joe running at 6.5 miles per hour and Joe is running at the speed of 8 miles per hour. How long does it take Joe to catch Jason?

    A. $3\ hours$
    B. $4\ hours$
    C. $6\ hours$
    D. $8\ hours$

33) 44 students took an exam and 11 of them failed. What percent of the students passed the exam?

    A. 20%
    B. 40%
    C. 60%
    D. 75%

34) If $f(x) = 2x^3 + 5x^2 + 2x$ and $g(x) = -3$, what is the value of $f(g(x))$?

    A. 36
    B. 32
    C. 24
    D. -15

35) The diagonal of a rectangle is 10 inches long and the height of the rectangle is 6 inches. What is the perimeter of the rectangle?

    A. $10\ inches$
    B. $12\ inches$
    C. $16\ inches$
    D. $28\ inches$

36) The perimeter of the trapezoid below is $40\ cm$. What is its area?

    A. $48\ cm^2$
    B. $98\ cm^2$
    C. $140\ cm^2$
    D. $576\ cm^2$

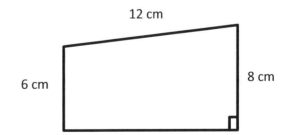

37) If $f(x)=2x^3+2$ and $(x)=\frac{1}{x}$, what is the value of $f(g(x))$?

   A. $\frac{1}{2x^3+2}$

   B. $\frac{2}{x^3}$

   C. $\frac{1}{2x}$

   D. $\frac{2}{x^3}+2$

38) A cruise line ship left Port A and traveled 80 miles due west and then 150 miles due north.

   At this point, what is the shortest distance from the cruise to port A?

   A. 70 miles

   B. 80 miles

   C. 150 miles

   D. 170 miles

39) If the ratio of $5a$ to $2b$ is $\frac{1}{10}$, what is the ratio of a to b?

   A. 10

   B. 25

   C. $\frac{1}{25}$

   D. $\frac{1}{20}$

40) If $x=9$, what is the value of y in the following equation? $2y=\frac{2x^2}{3}+6$

   A. 30

   B. 45

   C. 60

   D. 120

41) If $\frac{x-3}{5}=N$ and $N=6$, what is the value of x?

   A. 25

   B. 28

   C. 30

   D. 33

42) Which of the following is equal to $b^{\frac{3}{5}}$?

A. $\sqrt{b^{\frac{5}{3}}}$

B. $b^{\frac{5}{3}}$

C. $\sqrt[5]{b^3}$

D. $\sqrt[3]{b^5}$

43) On Saturday, Sara read N pages of a book each hour for 3 hours, and Mary read M pages of a book each hour for 4 hours. Which of the following represents the total number of pages of book read by Sara and Mary on Saturday?

A. $12MN$

B. $3N + 4M$

C. $7MN$

D. $4N + 3M$

44) Sara opened a bank account that earns 2 percent compounded annually. Her initial deposit was \$150, and she uses the expression $\$150(x)^n$ to find the value of the account after n years. What is the value of x in the expression?

A. 0.02

B. 0.20

C. 20%

D. 1.02

45) If function is defined as $f(x) = bx^2 + 15$, and b is a constant and $f(2) = 35$. What is the value of $f(5)$?

A. 25

B. 35

C. 140

D. 165

46) Find the solution (x, y) to the following system of equations?
$$2x + 5y = 11$$
$$4x - 2y = -14$$

A. $(14, 5)$

B. $(6, 8)$

C. $(11, 17)$

D. $(-2, 3)$

47) Calculate $f(4)$ for the function $f(x) = 3x^2 - 4$.

A. 44

B. 40

C. 38

D. 30

48) What are the zeroes of the function $f(x) = x^3 + 5x^2 + 6x$?

    A.   0
    B.   2
    C.   0, 2, 3
    D.   0, −2, −3

49) Which of the following lines is parallel to: $6y - 2x = 24$?
    A. $y = \frac{1}{3}x + 2$
    B. $y = 3x + 5$
    C. $y = x - 2$
    D. $y = 2x - 1$

50) The average of $13, 15, 20$ and x is 20. What is the value of x?
    A.   9
    B.   15
    C.   18
    D.   32

End of CHSPE Math Practice Test

CHSPE Mathematics Practice Test Answers and Explanations

Now, it's time to review your results to see where you went wrong and what areas you need to improve!

CHSPE Math Practice Test 1					
1	C	21	D	41	D
2	D	22	D	42	C
3	D	23	B	43	B
4	D	24	A	44	D
5	B	25	D	45	C
6	C	26	A	46	D
7	D	27	D	47	A
8	C	28	B	48	D
9	B	29	C	49	A
10	D	30	D	50	D
11	B	31	C		
12	D	32	C		
13	C	33	D		
14	D	34	D		
15	B	35	D		
16	B	36	B		
17	D	37	D		
18	A	38	D		
19	C	39	C		
20	D	40	A		

CHSPE Mathematics Practice Test Answers and Explanations

1) Choice C is correct

$$average\ (mean) = \frac{\text{sum of terms}}{\text{number of terms}} \Rightarrow 90 = \frac{sum\ of\ terms}{50} \Rightarrow sum = 90 \times 50 = 4500$$

The difference of 94 and 69 is 25. Therefore, 25 should be subtracted from the sum.

$$4500 - 25 = 4475,\ mean = \frac{\text{sum of terms}}{\text{number of terms}} \Rightarrow mean = \frac{4475}{50} = 89.5$$

2) Choice D is correct

For sum of 5: $(1\ \&\ 4)\ and\ (4\ \&\ 1), (2\ \&\ 3)$ and $(3\ \&\ 2)$, therefore we have 4 options.
For sum of 8: $(5\ \&\ 3) and\ (3\ \&\ 5), (4\ \&\ 4)$ and $(2\ \&\ 6)$, and $(6\ \&\ 2)$,we have 5 options. To get a sum of 5 or 8 for two dice: $4 + 5 = 9$.Since, we have $6 \times 6 = 36$ total number of options, the probability of getting a sum of 5 and 8 is 9 out of 36 or $\frac{9}{36} = \frac{1}{4}$

3) Choice D is correct

Use FOIL method. $(5x + 2y)(2x - y) = 10x^2 - 5xy + 4xy - 2y^2 = 10x^2 - xy - 2y^2$

4) Choice D is correct

To solve absolute values equations, write two equations. $x - 10$ could be positive 4, or negative 4. Therefore, $x - 10 = 4 \Rightarrow x = 14$, $x - 10 = -4 \Rightarrow x = 6$. Find the product of solutions: $6 \times 14 = 84$

5) Choice B is correct

The equation of a line in slope intercept form is: $y = mx + b$. Solve for y.

$4x - 2y = 6 \Rightarrow -2y = 6 - 4x \Rightarrow y = (6 - 4x) \div (-2) \Rightarrow y = 2x - 3$. The slope is 2.

The slope of the line perpendicular to this line is: $m_1 \times m_2 = -1 \Rightarrow 2 \times m_2 = -1 \Rightarrow m_2 = -\frac{1}{2}$.

6) Choice C is correct

Plug in the value of x and y. $x = 3$ and $y = -2$.

$6(x - 2y) + (2 - x)^2 = 6(3 - 2(-2)) + (2 - 3)^2 = 6(3 + 4) + (-1)^2 = 42 + 1 = 43$

7) Choice D is correct

Use formula of rectangle prism volume.$V = (length)\ (width)\ (height) \Rightarrow 2500 = (25)\ (10)\ (height) \Rightarrow height = 2500 \div 250 = 10$

8) Choice C is correct

$$4 \div \frac{1}{3} = 12$$

9) Choice B is correct

The diagonal of the square is 4. Let x be the side. Use Pythagorean Theorem: $a^2 + b^2 = c^2$

$$x^2 + x^2 = 4^2 \Rightarrow 2x^2 = 4^2 \Rightarrow 2x^2 = 16 \Rightarrow x^2 = 8 \Rightarrow x = \sqrt{8}$$

The area of the square is: $\sqrt{8} \times \sqrt{8} = 8$

10) Choice D is correct

Solve for the sum of five numbers.

$$average = \frac{sum\ of\ terms}{number\ of\ terms} \Rightarrow 26 = \frac{sum\ of\ 5\ numbers}{5} \Rightarrow sum\ of\ 5\ numbers = 26 \times 5 = 130$$

The sum of 5 numbers is 130. If a sixth number 42 is added, then the sum of 6 numbers is

$$130 + 42 = 172.\ average = \frac{sum\ of\ terms}{number\ of\ terms} = \frac{172}{6} = 28.66$$

11) Choice B is correct

ratio of A: $\frac{570}{600} = 0.95$ ratio of B: $\frac{291}{300} = 0.97$ ratio of C: $\frac{665}{700} = 0.95$ ratio of D: $\frac{528}{550} = 0.96$

The maximum ratio is 0.97.

12) Choice D is correct

First find percentage of men in city A and percentage of women in city C. Percentage of men in

city A $= \frac{600}{1170}$ and percentage of women in city C $= \frac{665}{1365}$. Find the ratio and simplify. $\frac{\frac{600}{1170}}{\frac{665}{1365}} = \frac{20}{19}$

13) Choice C is correct

$$\frac{528 + x}{550} = 1.2 \to 528 + x = 660 \to x = 132$$

14) Choice D is correct

Jason needs an 70% average to pass for five exams. Therefore, the sum of 5 exams must be at lease $5 \times 70 = 350$. The sum of 4 exams is: $68 + 72 + 85 + 90 = 315$.

The minimum score Jason can earn on his fifth and final test to pass is: $350 - 315 = 35$

15) Choice B is correct

Isolate and solve for $x.\frac{2}{3}x + \frac{1}{6} = \frac{1}{2} \Rightarrow \frac{2}{3}x = \frac{1}{2} - \frac{1}{6} = \frac{1}{3} \Rightarrow \frac{2}{3}x = \frac{1}{3}$ .Multiply both sides by the reciprocal of the coefficient of x. $(\frac{3}{2})\frac{2}{3}x = \frac{1}{3}(\frac{3}{2}) \Rightarrow x = \frac{3}{6} = \frac{1}{2}$

16) Choice B is correct

Use simple interest formula: $I = prt$ (I = interest, p = principal, r = rate, t = time).

$$I = (12,000)(0.045)(2) = 1,080$$

17) Choice D is correct

Simplify. $7x^2y^3(2x^2y)^3 = 7x^2y^3(8x^6y^3) = 56x^8y^6$

18) Choice A is correct

Surface Area of a cylinder = $2\pi r\ (r + h)$,The radius of the cylinder is 2 (4 ÷ 2) inches and its height is 8 inches. Therefore, Surface Area of a cylinder = 2π (2) (2 + 8) = $40\ \pi$

19) Choice C is correct

Three times of 25,000 is 75,000. One sixth of them cancelled their tickets. One sixth of 75,000 equals 12,500 ($\frac{1}{6} \times 75000 = 12500$). 62,500 (75000 − 12000 = 62500) fans are attending this week.

20) Choice D is correct

The area of the square is 49 inches. Therefore, the side of the square is square root of the area.

$\sqrt{49}$ = 7 inches. Four times the side of the square is the perimeter: $4 \times 7 = 28\ inches$

21) Choice D is correct

$g(x) = -4,$ **then** $f\bigl(g(x)\bigr) = f(-4) = 2\ (-4)^3 + 5(-4)^2 + 2(-4) = -128 + 80 - 8 = -56$

22) Choice D is correct

Use the information provided in the question to draw the shape.

Use Pythagorean Theorem: $a^2 + b^2 = c^2$

$50^2 + 120^2 = c^2 \Rightarrow 2,500 + 14,400 = c^2 \Rightarrow 16,900 = c^2 \Rightarrow c = 130$

23) Choice B is correct

Plug in 104 for F and then solve for C.

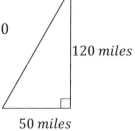

Port A

120 miles

50 miles

$C = \dfrac{5}{9}\ (F - 32) \Rightarrow C = \dfrac{5}{9}\ (104 - 32) \Rightarrow C = \dfrac{5}{9}\ (72) = 40$

24) Choice A is correct

The width of the rectangle is twice its length. Let x be the length. Then, $width = 2x$

Perimeter of the rectangle is $2 \, (width \, + \, length) = 2(2x + x) = 72 \Rightarrow 6x = 72 \Rightarrow x = 12$. Length of the rectangle is 12 meters.

25) Choice D is correct

$average = \dfrac{\text{sum of terms}}{\text{number of terms}} \Rightarrow$ (average of 6 numbers) $14 = \dfrac{\text{sum of numbers}}{6} \Rightarrow$ sum of 6 numbers is $14 \times 6 = 84$, (average of 4 numbers) $10 = \dfrac{\text{sum of numbers}}{4} \Rightarrow$ sum of 4 numbers is $10 \times 4 = 40$. $sum \, of \, 6 \, numbers - sum \, of \, 4 \, numbers = sum \, of \, 2 \, numbers$,

$84 - 40 = 44$ average of 2 numbers $= \dfrac{44}{2} = 22$

26) Choice A is correct

First, find the number. Let x be the number. Write the equation and solve for x. 150% of a number is 75, then:$1.5 \times x = 75 \Rightarrow x = 75 \div 1.5 = 50$, 80% of 50 is:$0.8 \times 50 = 40$

27) Choice D is correct

Solve for y.$4x - 2y = 12 \Rightarrow -2y = 12 - 4x \Rightarrow y = 2x - 6$. The slope of the line is 2.

28) Choice B is correct

the population is increased by 10% and 20%. 10% increase changes the population to 110% of original population. For the second increase, multiply the result by 120%.

$(1.10) \times (1.20) = 1.32 = 132\%$. 32 percent of the population is increased after two years.

29) Choice C is correct

The formula for the area of the circle is: $A = \pi r^2$,**The area is** 36π. **Therefore:**$A = \pi r^2 \Rightarrow 6\pi = \pi r^2$, **Divide both sides by** π: $36 = r^2 \Rightarrow r = 6$. Diameter of a circle is $2 \times$ radius. Then:

$Diameter = 2 \times 6 = 12$

30) Choice D is correct

If 20% of a number is 4, what is the number: 20% $of \, x = 4 \Rightarrow 0.20 \, x = 4 \Rightarrow x = 4 \div 0.20 = 20$

31) Choice C is correct

Write a proportion and solve for x.$\dfrac{3}{2} = \dfrac{x}{26} \Rightarrow 2x = 3 \times 26 \Rightarrow x = 39 \, ft$

32) Choice C is correct

The distance between Jason and Joe is 9 *miles*. Jason running at 6.5 *miles per hour* and Joe is running at the speed of 8 *miles per hour*. Therefore, every hour the distance is 1.5 *miles* less.

$9 \div 1.5 = 6$

33) Choice D is correct

The failing rate is 11 out of $44 = \frac{11}{44}$, Change the fraction to percent: $\frac{11}{44} \times 100\% = 25\%$. 25 percent of students failed. Therefore, 75 percent of students passed the exam.

34) Choice D is correct

$g(x) = -3$, **then** $f(g(x)) = f(-3) = 2(-3)^3 + 5(-3)^2 + 2(-3) = -54 + 45 - 6 = -15$

35) Choice D is correct

Let x be the width of the rectangle. Use Pythagorean Theorem:

$a^2 + b^2 = c^2$

$x^2 + 6^2 = 10^2 \Rightarrow x^2 + 36 = 100 \Rightarrow x^2 = 100 - 36 = 64 \Rightarrow x = 8$

Perimeter of the rectangle $= 2\,(length\ +\ width) = 2\,(8\ +\ 6)\ =\ 2\,(14)\ =\ 28$

36) Choice B is correct

The perimeter of the trapezoid is 40. herefore, the missing side (height) is

$= 40 - 8 - 12 - 6 = 14$. Area of a trapezoid: $A\ =\ \frac{1}{2}\,h\,(b_1\ +\ b_2)\ =\ \frac{1}{2}\,(14)\,(6+8)\ =\ 98$

37) Choice D is correct

$f(g(x)) = 2 \times (\frac{1}{x})^3 + 2 = \frac{2}{x^3} + 2$

38) Choice D is correct

Use the information provided in the question to draw the shape.

Use Pythagorean Theorem: $a^2 + b^2 = c^2$

$80^2 + 150^2 = c^2 \Rightarrow 6400 + 22500 = c^2 \Rightarrow 28900 = c^2 \Rightarrow c\ =\ 170$

39) Choice C is correct

Write the ratio of $5a$ to $2b$. $\frac{5a}{2b} = \frac{1}{10}$. Use cross multiplication and then simplify.

$5a \times 10 = 2b \times 1 \rightarrow 50a = 2b \rightarrow a = \frac{2b}{50} = \frac{b}{25}$

150 miles

Port A

80 miles

Now, find the ratio of a to b. $\frac{a}{b} = \frac{\frac{b}{25}}{b} \rightarrow \frac{b}{25} \div b = \frac{b}{25} \times \frac{1}{b} = \frac{b}{25b} = \frac{1}{25}$

40) Choice A is correct

Plug in the value of x in the equation and solve for y. $2y = \frac{2x^2}{3} + 6 \rightarrow 2y = \frac{2(9)^2}{3} + 6 \rightarrow$

$$2y = \frac{2(81)}{3} + 6 \rightarrow 2y = 54 + 6 = 60 \rightarrow 2y = 60 \rightarrow y = 30$$

41) Choice D is correct

Since $N = 6$, substitute 6 for N in the equation $\frac{x-3}{5} = N$, which gives $\frac{x-3}{5} = 6$. Multiplying both sides of $\frac{x-3}{5} = 6$ by 5 gives $x - 3 = 30$ and then adding 3 to both sides of $x - 3 = 30$ then, $x = 33$.

42) Choice C is correct

$b^{\frac{m}{n}} = \sqrt[n]{b^m}$ For any positive integers m and n. Thus, $b^{\frac{3}{5}} = \sqrt[5]{b^3}$

43) Choice B is correct

The total number of pages read by Sara is 3 (hours she spent reading) multiplied by her rate of reading: $\frac{Npages}{hour} \times 3hours = 3N$

Similarly, the total number of pages read by Mary is 4 (hours she spent reading) multiplied by her rate of reading: $\frac{Mpages}{hour} \times 4hours = 4M$ the total number of pages read by Sara and Mary is the sum of the total number of pages read by Sara and the total number of pages read by Mary: $3N + 4M$.

44) Choice D is correct

The initial deposit earns 2 percent interest compounded annually. Thus, at the end of year 1, the new value of the account is the initial deposit of $150 plus 2 percent of the initial deposit:

$\$150 + \frac{2}{100}(\$150) = \$150(1.02)$.

Since the interest is compounded annually, the value at the end of each succeeding year is the sum of the previous year's value plus 2 percent of the previous year's value. This is equivalent to multiplying the previous year's value by 1.02. Thus, after 2 years, the value will be $\$150(1.02)(1.02) = \$(150)(1.02)^2$; and after 3 years, the value will be $(150)(1.02)^3$; and after n years, the value will be $(150)(1.02)^n$. Therefore, in the formula for the value for Sara's account after n years $(100)(x)^n$, the value of x is 1.02.

45) Choice C is correct

First find the value of b, and then find $f(5)$. Since $f(2) = 35$, substuting 2 for x and 35 for $f(x)$ gives $35 = b(2)^2 + 15 = 4b + 15$. Solving this equation gives $b = 5$. Thus

$$f(x) = 5x^2 + 15, \quad f(5) = 5(5)^2 + 15 \rightarrow f(5) = 125 + 15, \quad f(3) = 140$$

46) Choice D is correct

Solving Systems of Equations by Elimination: Multiply the first equation by (-2), then add it to the second equation.

$$\begin{array}{l} -2(2x + 5y = \ 11) \\ \underline{\quad 4x - 2y = -14 \quad} \end{array} \Rightarrow \begin{array}{l} -4x - 10y = -22 \\ \underline{\quad 4x - 2y = -14 \quad} \end{array} \Rightarrow -12y = -36 \Rightarrow y = 3$$

Plug in the value of y into one of the equations and solve for x.

$$2x + 5(3) = \ 11 \Rightarrow 2x + 15 = \ 11 \Rightarrow 2x = \ -4 \Rightarrow x = \ -2$$

47) Choice A is correct

Identify the input value. Since the function is in the form $f(x)$ and the question asks to calculate $f(4)$, the input value is four. $f(4) \rightarrow x = 4$, Using the function, input the desired x value. Now substitute 4 in for every x in the function. $f(x) = 3x^2 - 4$, $f(4) = 3(4)^2 - 4$, $f(4) = 48 - 4$, $f(4) = 44$

48) Choice D is correct

Frist factor the function: $f(x) = x^3 + 5x^2 + 6x = x\ (x + 2)(x + 3)$, **To find the zeros,** $f(x)$ **should be zero.** $f(x) = x\ (x + 2)(x + 3) = 0$, **Therefore, the zeros are:** $x = 0$, $(x + 2) = 0 \Rightarrow x = \ -2, (x + 3) = 0 \Rightarrow x = \ -3$

49) Choice A is correct

First write the equation in slope intercept form. Add $2x$ to both sides to get $6y = 2x + 24$. Now divide both sides by 6 to get $y = \frac{1}{3}x + 4$. The slope of this line is $\frac{1}{3}$, so any line that also has a slope of $\frac{1}{3}$ would be parallel to it. Only choice A has a slope of $\frac{1}{3}$.

50) Choice D is correct

$$average = \frac{sum\ of\ terms}{number\ of\ terms} \Rightarrow 20 = \frac{13 + 15 + 20 + x}{4} \Rightarrow 80 = 48 + x \Rightarrow x = 32$$

Receive the PDF version of this book or get another FREE book!

Thank you for using our Book!

Do you LOVE this book?

Then, you can get the PDF version of this book or another book absolutely FREE!

Please email us at:

info@EffortlessMath.com

for details.

Author's Final Note

I hope you enjoyed reading this book. You've made it through the book! Great job!

First of all, thank you for purchasing this study guide. I know you could have picked any number of books to help you prepare for your CHSPE Math test, but you picked this book and for that I am extremely grateful.

It took me years to write this study guide for the CHSPE Math because I wanted to prepare a comprehensive CHSPE Math study guide to help test takers make the most effective use of their valuable time while preparing for the test.

After teaching and tutoring math for over a decade, I've gathered my personal notes and lessons to develop this study guide. It is my greatest hope that the lessons in this book could help you prepare for your test successfully.

If you have any questions, please contact me at reza@effortlessmath.com and I will be glad to assist. Your feedback will help me to greatly improve the quality of my books in the future and make this book even better. Furthermore, I expect that I have made a few minor errors somewhere in this study guide. If you think this to be the case, please let me know so I can fix the issue as soon as possible.

If you enjoyed this book and found some benefit in reading this, I'd like to hear from you and hope that you could take a quick minute to post a review on the book's Amazon page. To leave your valuable feedback, please visit: amzn.to/2OqVOMy

Or scan this QR code.

I personally go over every single review, to make sure my books really are reaching out and helping students and test takers. Please help me help CHSPE Math test takers, by leaving a review!

I wish you all the best in your future success!

Reza Nazari

Math teacher and author

Made in the USA
Las Vegas, NV
09 April 2021